Bessie Bibbs' Ginormous Fibs

By Chris Jones   Illustrated by Claire Bell

First Published 2021 by Yearn to Learn Children's Books

ISBN 978-0-9574392-6-9

Text Copyright © Chris Jones 2021

Illustrations Copyright © Claire Bell 2021

Dear Mums, Dads, Grandparents...

We really hope your family enjoy reading about our latest monster Bessie Bibbs – a loveable rogue who just can't stop herself from getting into scrapes.

Bessie is the second monster in our Hoppity Thicket series - the first was Red Spotted Ned. And we've got more in the pipeline too, each with their own little nuance and story to tell.

We believe passionately in the power of reading - for all ages. We've deliberately used vocabulary that is real and occasionally challenging. So, if your child asks what certain words mean, then we think that's good because it will develop their active mind.

We have a website - yearntolearn.co.uk where you can discover what we're doing next. You can also find us on Facebook and Instagram (@yearntolearnbooks) where we post regular fun verses and random stuff. Come and check us out!

Finally, getting seen as a newbie indie author is so hard and your help would be really welcome. Wherever you bought this book, please leave us a review – they mean the world to us!

Thank you so much, Chris and Claire x

Map of Hoppity Thicket

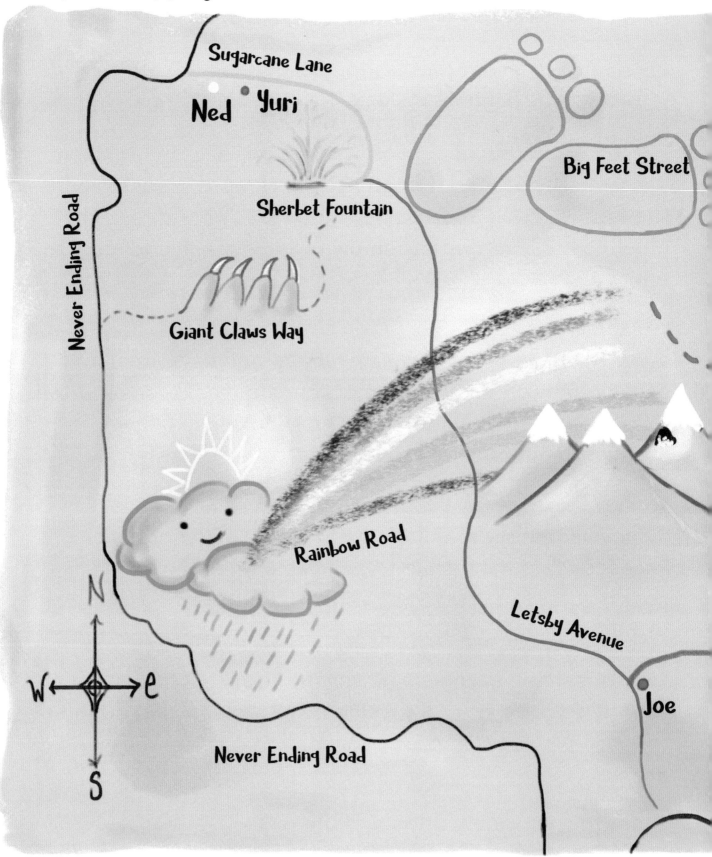

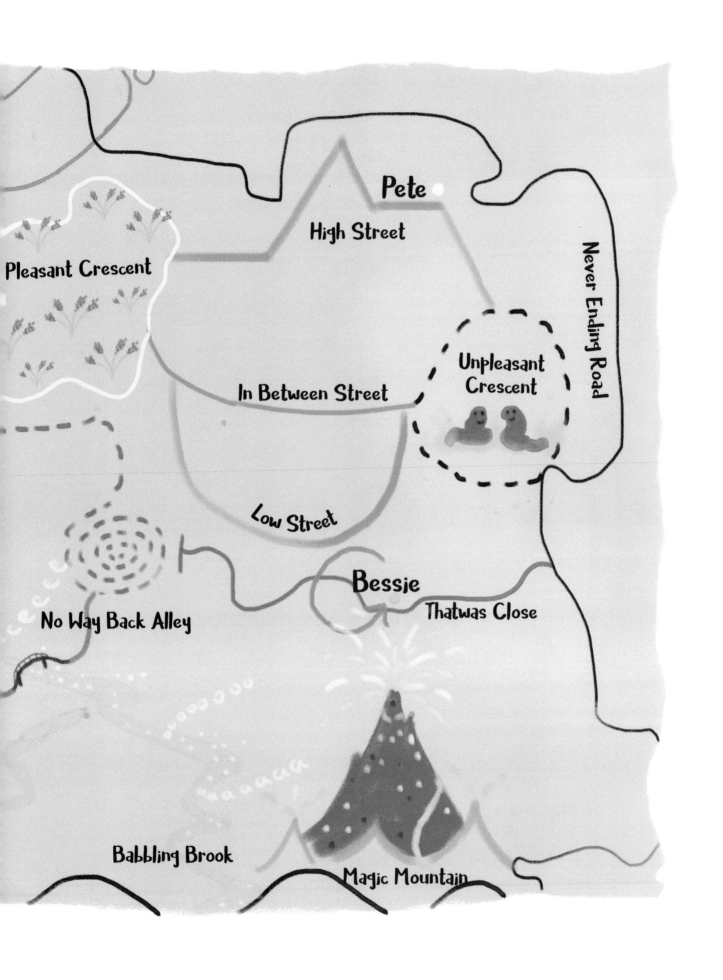

In the town of Hoppity Thicket,
lives the monster, Bessie Bibbs.
And all this lady wants to do,
is tell ginormous fibs!

The type of fibbers we might know,
tell stories wide and tall.
But Bessie's one of those you'd call,
a blessed know-it-all!

Every day at two o-clock,
    this monster takes a walk.
And one thing you can guarantee,
    she'll always stop and talk.

2

The story you're about to hear,
happened not so long ago.
It was on her daily travels where,
she met her cousin Joe.

His job is with computers,
he really is quite smart.
But now he's got a problem cos,
his blinkin' car won't start!

"Hello Joe", Bessie said,
   "you're not looking great?"
"This heap of junk, just won't work,
   it's gonna make me late!"

"Oh, let me help!" Bessie cried,
"I'm an excellent mechanic.
I'll get you to your meeting Joe,
no need at all to panic."

She rolled her sleeves and got to work,
testing pipes, unplugging wires.
"I'll need your set of spanners, Joe,
a hammer and some pliers."

When the car was all in pieces,
Joe looked quite concerned.
Bit by bit, it all went back,
his engine had returned.

"Time to get you moving Joe,
get the key and start her up."
But as he turned the motor,
all they heard was 'hypp' and 'schlupp'!

As smoke and fumes engulfed them,
Joe's face was crimson red.
Before she came it wouldn't start,
but now it just looked dead!

"There must be something bigger,
behind this disarray.
I'd love to stay and help some more,
but I'D BEST be on my way."

At breakneck speed, Bessie fled,
    oh how she'd dropped a clanger!
She sped off down the pavement,
    as Joe looked on in anger.

She came onto the High Street,
    and spied old Plumber Pete.
Waiting tensely at his gate,
    his visitor to greet.

"Hello there, Pete" Bessie said,
    "you're looking quite dismayed?"
"My computer's gone and broken,
    but it seems Joe's been delayed."

Bessie paused and blushed a bit,
but then a plan she chose.
"I can fix computers Pete,
I taught Joe all he knows!"

12

They went inside and there it sat,
a deathly blank blue screen.
"Don't you worry, Plumber Pete,
I'll sort out your machine."

Pete went to make a coffee,
as Bessie got to work.
She started pressing buttons,
but then it went berserk!

With a growing sense of panic,
Bessie tried a hard reset.
But when it started whirring,
she broke into a sweat.

In a state of desperation,
  she lunged and pulled the plugs.
Just as Plumber Pete came back,
  with steaming coffee mugs.

16

"There must be something bigger,
    behind this disarray.
I'd love to stay and help some more,
    but I SHOULD be on my way."

Once again, she left in haste,
   a second mess created.
"What awful luck," Bessie thought,
   her mood now quite deflated.

            Pete looked out from the doorway,
               as she took off down the hill.
            Ten yards back - Computer Joe,
               oh, if looks could kill!

18

From all this stress and hurried steps,
Bessie's fit to drop.
With mouth so dry and feet so sore,
she spied the coffee shop.

DRINKS
Flat White 5   Latte 6
Espresso   4.5 Fluffy 1
Monsta Mash 7   Fur Tea 4
Hot chocolate 5 Water 5

To her surprise, the shop was bare,
something was afoot.
"Coffee's off," said owner Gill,
"my machine – it's gone kaput".

Well ... you and I - we'd know by now,
    not to interfere.
But as you've seen, it's not her way,
    to suffer doubt and fear.

"I can help you fix it Gill,
    machines are what I do.
Worry not, I'll come on through,
    and get this thing to brew."

"Are you sure?" asked owner Gill,
   "it's really quite complex."
"Not to me," Bessie smiled,
   "I'll start with simple checks."

She pressed the knobs, she moved the dials,
   then stared at it some more.
"I wonder what this pipe does,
   that feeds into the floor?"

"I think I know the problem,
it's this without a doubt."
But as she turned the screw a touch,
the water flooded out!

23

"WHAT HAVE YOU DONE?!", said owner Gill,
"could I get much GLUMMER?
Instead of a mechanic,
now I need a PLUMBER!"

"There must be something bigger,
    behind this disarray.
I'd love to stay and help some more,
    but I MUST be on my way."

Yet again, Bessie's fibs
    had caused a holy mess.
In came Plumber Pete and Joe,
    in fits of rage and stress.

"I heard you'd sprung a leak?" said Pete,
 "it's looking kinda messy.
Let us guess the problem...
 it's Bessie! ... Bessie! ... Bessie!"

"She needs to learn a lesson,
    and I know just how she can.
I'll ring up my friend Edna,
    who owns the ice cream van."

"Of course, I'll help", Edna said,
    as their cunning plan commences.
"It's time that Bessie understood,
    her actions have consequences."

Edna called up Bessie,
   "I hear you're an expert fixer?"
"What's the problem?", Bessie asked.
   "It's my bloomin' ice cream mixer."

Several minutes later,
   and Bessie's on the job.
But hiding in the bushes sits
   a very angry mob!

Bessie stood there once again,
another puzzle to solve.
A mass of pipes and hoses,
were testing her resolve.

She fiddled with the switches,
    and looked into the spout.
Then as she turned a knob half-way,
    ice cream spurted out!

Her face was truly covered,
   her clothes were soaking wet.
But as she turned to Edna,
35   familiar faces met.

"Now's the time to tell you,
    you're a MENACE Bessie Bibbs!
Although we know you just mean well,
    you MUST stop telling fibs."

"You're NOT an expert fixer.
    Much havoc do you wreak.
So next time someone might need help,
    just turn the other cheek."

36

Bessie said she's sorry,
   would now leave well alone.
Then Edna went into her van,
   and brought each one a cone.

So, if you're ever in their town,
and need a helping hand.
If this one jumps into the fray,
remind her she is **BANNED!**

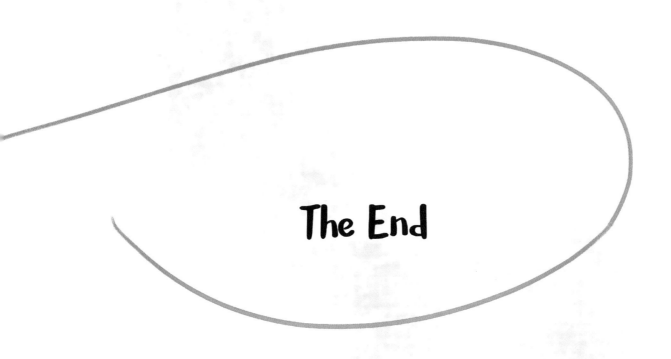

The End

Other books by Chris Jones

Princess Pea of Popty Ping

Explore the magical world of Benjamin Peel's garden.

Our heroine, Penelope, meets the charming Prince Winkle when he rolls down a deadly ravine. He's just rescued a young boy called Colin from the clutches of a band of giants.

So unfolds a story of romance, adventure and magic.

Harley Hound

Harley is a basset hound. And being a basset hound brings certain challenges!

Then one day, something momentous happens! Suddenly, Harley can be the dog she'd always dreamt of being. She can do the things she sees other dogs do – carry huge sticks, fly through the air to catch balls … even intimidate other dogs.

However, being someone she's not isn't all she'd imagined. Because others like her just the way she is…

Did you know there are only around 700 hawksbill turtles left on the planet? Myrtle is one such turtle.

Join us on her eventful journey as she learns to cope with loss and adversity.

This beautiful and heart-warming story introduces the impact of climate change and conservation, but in an upbeat way. Children will feel inspired to make a positive difference and be left with hope, rather than despair.

Red Spotted Ned

Ned is a spotted monster. A very angry spotted monster. And when he gets mad – which is most of the time – his spots turn an angry shade of red.

The brunt of his ire is mild-mannered next door neighbour Yuri, who just wants to make Ned happy. Can Ned change his ways and become the loveable, green-spotted monster Yuri believes he secretly is?

The first book in 'The Monstrous World of Hoppity Thicket' series.

About the author

For as long as he can remember, Chris has had a huge passion for storytelling. When his son Jesse was a young boy, instead of reading bedtime stories, they would make up their own far-fetched tales around the fictional superhero Deadly Derek.

2021 has marked Chris's entry into children's picture book writing. And he's been busy, publishing five fantastic books over the year. His talent for writing original and captivating stories around powerful messages is so evident – a rising star for sure!

Besides having a great story to tell, Chris believes the best children's picture books have three key ingredients. The first is natural rhyme - words that feel like they should be there, not just because they match with another. The second is tantalising words and grammar - Chris's books will stretch a younger reader's vocabulary, and he uses a variety of tools to make the words roll off the tongue. And the final ingredient? Well, they must have beautiful illustrations to bring the story to life. For this, he relies totally on the genius of Claire Bell and her wonderful visual translation of his verses.

Printed in Great Britain
by Amazon

~ FOREWORD ~

The First Sea Lord, Sir Mark Stanhope, KC.

FOR too long, Vice-Admiral The Lord Collingwood's reputation has been to some extent eclipsed by that of his iconic contemporary and close friend, Horatio Nelson. Inspirational as Nelson's examples of leadership and courage in battle undoubtedly are, it is often overlooked that Collingwood's contribution at the Battle of Trafalgar was vitally important. His ship, HMS *Royal Sovereign,* led the charge and was the first to open fire. "See," said Nelson, pointing to the *Royal Sovereign* as she penetrated the centre of the enemy's line, "see how that noble fellow Collingwood carries his ship into action!" After Nelson had been fatally wounded, it was Collingwood who assumed supreme command of the British fleet during the remainder of the battle to their ultimate victory.

Like Nelson, Collingwood had honed his skills and judgement in the course of a varied and exciting career which had taken him all over the world, from the West Indies to the Mediterranean. His career developed against a busy operational backdrop as Great Britain sought to protect her global interests, the inhabitants of her overseas territories and the trade upon which Britain's imperial ambition rested. There was also the small matter of deterring Napoleon's aggression.

In many respects, the role of the Royal Navy remains the same today. Our sailors and marines are not only to be found fighting in Afghanistan. Naval ships, submarines, aircraft and personnel are currently deployed worldwide conducting national and multinational operations which support the UK, promote its values and protect its interests and

economic prosperity. In the last 12 months alone, sailors and marines have been instrumental in intercepting major narcotic shipments in the Caribbean, off West Africa and in the Indian Ocean. Maritime security operations in the Mediterranean, the Arabian Sea and off the Horn of Africa continue to intercept illegal activity and reassure legitimate users of the high seas, enabling global trade to continue unhindered by pirates, traffickers and other criminals.

Naval units are permanently deployed in the South Atlantic in support of the Government's responsibilities to protect the Falkland Islands and our interests in Antarctica. At the same time, Royal Navy ships and aircraft continue to safeguard the integrity of UK Territorial Waters and Airspace, to provide counter terrorism support to the Home Office, to protect shipping, ports and offshore energy platforms, undertake inspection and enforcement action on behalf of the Marine and Fisheries Agency and conduct Search and Rescue operations around our coast. Last, but far from least, the Royal Navy has for the last 40 years also been responsible for delivering the Nation's Nuclear Deterrent.

I am delighted that the Royal Navy is so closely associated with this Festival, which celebrates and commemorates the life of a gifted naval officer whose many qualities we all hope to emulate. In remembering Collingwood and his achievements, we also have the opportunity to re-connect with our maritime heritage and understand how closely linked are the fortunes of this island nation and the Royal Navy that serves it.

~ ADMIRAL LORD COLLINGWOOD ~

A Biographical Sketch

CUTHBERT Collingwood was born in Newcastle upon Tyne in 1748 into a large family, the eldest of three sons. The Collingwoods were an old Northumbrian family, though the Admiral's father, also Cuthbert, was a trader without land or fortune.

The building in which the family lived, on the steep, narrow street called The Side, which leads from St Nicholas's Cathedral down towards the Quayside, has long gone. But above the doorway to Milburn House, just below the Black Gate, a plaque and a bust record its location. The castle and the city's walls are a continuing reminder that the Newcastle of Collingwood's day was still a border garrison whose gates and walls had been manned as recently as 1745 against the Jacobite rebellion.

(Courtesy: Newcastle upon Tyne Trinity House)

'Battle of Cape St Vincent' by J. W. Carmichael in collaboration with George Balmer. It was here that Collingwood saved Nelson's life.

But Newcastle was also an international city of trade. The Quayside bustled with shipping from across the world. Coals from the North-East's apparently inexhaustible mines were exported across the seven seas and in return came exotic spices from the Far East, tobacco from America, tea from India, sugar and rum from the West Indies.

But above all, and almost more precious than goods, was news — from Canada and Hanover, from Stettin and Petersburg and the Cape. Britain, flexing her imperial muscles as never before, was at the centre of the world and the imaginations of young boys growing up here were fired by the exploits of daring naval captains and heroic generals.

The oldest son of a trader might have been expected to follow his father into business. But the business was fail-

ing. The Collingwoods used their family connections to procure for Cuthbert and his brother Wilfred berths as midshipmen in the Royal Navy. Thus ended the future Admiral's short period of formal education at Newcastle's famous Royal Grammar School, where he had already become friends with John Scott, the future Lord Eldon.

The Collingwood boys went to sea in 1761 at the ages of 13 and 11 respectively in the 28-gun frigate *Shannon*, commanded by Robert Braithwaite, a relative of Mrs Collingwood. As midshipmen they would be trained as future officers and gentlemen. They would serve a long apprenticeship, with at least six years before they could be considered for examination as lieutenants. In Cuthbert's case he did not become lieutenant until the age of 27, after seeing his first action — the amphibious assault on Bunker Hill near Boston which signalled the start of the American War of Independence in 1775.

The first of Collingwood's legendary letters dates from this period, but his midshipman's journals, one of which survives from tours in the Mediterranean and West Indies, shows that his character was fully formed at an early age. He was conscientious and a gifted seaman. He had mastered navigation, was cool and brave under fire. What is more, he was a compassionate and deeply humane officer who hated flogging and grieved when he lost a shipmate. He was also, like his much younger friend Horatio Nelson, whom he first met in 1773, ambitious and zealous for the honour of the navy and the King.

England's future saviours first served together under Sir Peter Parker on the West Indies station in 1778. Nelson had achieved the rank of Post-Captain at the unusually young age of 20. Collingwood, now 30, was suffering as a lieutenant under a tyrannical and ineffective commander called Robert Haswell in the 14-gun sloop *Hornet*. Nelson persuaded Parker to bring Collingwood under his command, first as lieutenant in the frigate *Lowestoffe*, then as Commander in the brig *Badger*, and then as Post-Captain in *Hinchinbroke*. Because of the ladder system of seniority in the Royal Navy, Nelson would retain a few crucial months' seniority over his friend up until his death at Trafalgar 25 years later.

Their first adventure together was disastrous. Nelson, on more or less his own authority, accompanied an army expedition up the San Juan River (in modern Nicaragua) looking for a new route to the Pacific Ocean and he nearly died of fever. Collingwood, stationed at the mouth of the river in support, lost 180 of his 200 men to malaria and the 'yellow jack'. Nelson returned almost lifeless to England. Collingwood remained in the Indies and survived shipwreck in a great hurricane off Jamaica in 1781.

Nelson's and Collingwood's lives seemed intertwined. In 1784 they were stationed together again in the West Indies. Collingwood was based at English Harbour in Antigua, charged with stemming the now-illegal trade between the islands and the new United States. His zealous enforcement of the so-called Navigation Acts won him few friends among the merchants of the Caribbean.

His consolation was the company of the navy's commissioner in Antigua, John Moutray, and, perhaps even more, that of Mary Moutray, the commissioner's wife. She was educated and intelligent, delightful company and a gifted hostess. When Nelson came out to join Collingwood these twin epitomes of England's naval officer class were united in their determination to stamp out smuggling, and united in their affection for Mrs Moutray. She was eventually forced to return to England with her ailing husband, but the two men remained friends with her for the rest of their lives.

Collingwood himself returned to England in 1786 and spent the only significant period of his life ashore. A year after leaving the West Indies he received the devastating news in a touching letter from Nelson that Wilfred, his brother and fellow captain, had died of an illness. When he was not in London using his connections to try to get another ship (in peace-time there was tremendous competition for each command as much of the fleet was laid-up) he was at home in Northumberland.

The young Cuthbert Collingwood kept meticulous logs of his voyages. He drew this picture of Funchal harbour when he arrived in Madeira in HMS Portland in March 1773.

Bonaparte's statue at Ajaccio, Corsica. His ambition to destroy British naval power was thwarted at Trafalgar.

(Courtesy: Susan Collingwood-Cameron)

Such was the status of a captain in the Navy, and so impressive a man had Collingwood become after nearly 20 years at sea, that he was able to successfully court the daughter of the Mayor of Newcastle, Sarah Blackett, whom he married in 1791. They went to live in Morpeth, in the house that still bears his name on Oldgate on the banks of the River Wansbeck. They had two daughters, little Sarah and Mary Patience. For the rest of his life Collingwood's letters reveal the depth of affection in which he held his wife and the girls, his home in Morpeth, and the country and people of Northumberland. The old legend that he walked along the lanes of the county sowing acorns so that England's navy should never want for oak trees is true: he was an early and conspicuous conservationist.

The world was changing. Britain was having to adapt to the loss of her most precious colony. The industrial revolution was transforming her domestic landscape. Collingwood's fellow Northumbrians George Stephenson and William Hedley, still in their shorts, would become pioneers of the locomotive. Across the English Channel, a new revolution was brewing in France. Within two years the French would have executed their king and Britain would be at war. Neither Collingwood nor Nelson would survive that war.

Collingwood's long experience as a seaman and officer were put to good use. He was a consummate professional. His ability to read the mind of the enemy and of his own men was admired by all those who knew and served with him. He was reserved in public, acutely conscious of both his provincial origins and of the isolation that a senior officer must impose on himself. He could not be friends with junior officers, nor with the men of the lower decks. Nevertheless, his compassion for their welfare and his sense of community with comrades of all ranks is unmistakeable from both his correspondence and from the testimony of those whom he commanded. He was known to weep at the end of a commission when he had to pay his ship's company off; and there were wise heads at the Admiralty in London who knew that they could confidently send him troublemakers. Compassionate he may have been, but it was said that one of his looks of displeasure was worse than a dozen lashes at the gangway. He was not a man whose authority one would challenge.

Collingwood fought in his first great sea battle against the French in 1794 at the age of 46. He was captain on Admiral Bowyer's flagship *Barfleur,* a first-rate ship-of-the-line carrying 98 guns and more than 800 men. Known as the Glorious First of June, the battle was not in truth particularly glorious. The British fleet failed to intercept a grain convoy from America heading to France and the two fleets both retired with several ships badly damaged. More insulting than the result, from Collingwood's point of view, was that most of the captains in the British fleet received medals from the king. Collingwood, for reasons, he believed, of personal malice, did not. It was an almost unbearable professional blow in spite of the kind support he received from many colleagues, Nelson included.

Collingwood was unable to right this wrong for three years. During that time he served in the Mediterranean with Nelson under Sir John Jervis. Jervis's 15-strong squadron, though small, was now trained to a peak of sea-going efficiency and battle readiness, on permanent blockade of the French and Spanish fleets between Cadiz and Toulon. Collingwood, in the 74-gun HMS *Excellent,* was perfectly in agreement with Jervis that discipline and gunnery would be the secret to beating the enemy. Collingwood at this time trained his crews to fire an extraordinary three broadsides in three and a half minutes — a rate never bettered in the age of sail. In tribute, the Royal Navy's school of gunnery at Fareham is named HMS *Collingwood.*

Since 1794 the British had been developing new naval tactics at sea while the French and Spanish fleets kept safe in their harbours. Jervis, Nelson, Collingwood and other forward-thinking officers had begun to believe that the enemy must be annihilated by destroying its ships, permanently removing the threat of future fleet actions. Against a Spanish fleet of 25 ships off Cape St Vincent, at the extreme south-west corner of Portugal, they got their chance to prove their new ideas. Nelson, impetuous, attacked first but was soon in trouble and surrounded. Collingwood, blazing away, came to his rescue and destroyed four enemy ships in the process. Nelson won undying fame. Collingwood won two medals (the second to make up for the previous slight) and the admiration of his peers.

The following years were filled with hard sea-miles, endless blockade and hardship in all weathers, with only very short periods ashore and fewer at home. After the brief Peace of Amiens in 1802, at which time Collingwood became a rear admiral and saw his wife and children for the last time, the long, grinding build-up to the Trafalgar campaign saw him more or less continuously stationed off

~ THE TYNEMOUTH MONUMENT ~

IN August 1845, 35 years after his death, a monument to Admiral Lord Collingwood funded by public subscription, was unveiled on the cliffs above Prior's Haven at the mouth of the River Tyne.

wrapped bollard — was created by Northumbrian sculptor, John Graham Lough.

His work was completed in London and then shipped in 13 pieces to the Tyne where it was erected onto a 45-feet (13.5m) high marble-and-sandstone base and pedestal designed by architect John Dobson.

Its location on land donated by the Duke of Northumberland emphasises Collingwood's family connection with nearby North

Collingwood's Monument at Tynemouth.

Shields and allows the statue to be seen from the sea and the river.

The four 32-pound cannon on the walls flanking the wide flight of steps at the monument's base were salvaged from his flagship, *Royal Sovereign*, and shipped from Woolwich to be added to

The 23-feet (7m) tall statue of Collingwood — wearing a draped cloak and with his hand resting on a rope-

the monument in 1848. In 2001 this Grade II* listed monument was restored at a cost of £170,000.

Brest, blockading the French Atlantic fleet. Collingwood's letters during these years, alternately wistful, rhetorically anti-French, grumpy and indomitable, reveal a middle-aged man, old before his time through overwork and what these days we would call micro-management. He was indulgent to his

Black and white portrait engraving

midshipman and sailors, hard on his officers, unstinting in his duty. His only companion was his faithful dog Bounce, an almost perfect naval dog except for its dislike of gun-fire. Collingwood was known to sing poor Bounce to sleep in his own cot with Shakes-pearean sonnets adapted to canine sensibilities. If long years of war and service had worn him to a thread, his famous wit survived intact. His put-downs were the stuff of legend and his correspondence, especially with his sisters and sis-ters-in-law, is full or charm and gos-sip. His handwriting, almost to the end, was perfect copperplate with a flourish of the tail on every 'd'.

In the summer of 1805 Collingwood pulled off a mas-terstroke. Blockading the Spanish fleet in Cadiz with just four ships, he found himself one morning confronted with Admiral Villeneuve's French battle fleet, newly arrived from the Indies having given Nelson the slip. Collingwood managed to convince the French, without firing a shot, that he had waiting just over the horizon a large number of reinforcements and, after what must have been a horri-bly tense few hours, shepherded them into Cadiz where they remained, cooped up, until the morning before Trafalgar: 21st October, 1805.

Nelson's fate in that battle is famous. Collingwood's, at the head of the lee column of battle, was to be first into the fight and last out of it, with fifty dead and many more wounded. Surviving his friend and comrade, Collingwood found himself at the age of 57 in command of the British fleet of 27 ships of the line, most of them virtually wrecks. That no British ship was lost in the hurricane that fol-lowed is an almost miraculous testament to seamanship and raw courage; that Collingwood felt forced to sink or burn all the enemy prizes (depriving the officers and men of the fleet of small fortunes) proved a decision which attracted the highest praise of his superiors and the ever-lasting enmity of some of his captains.

The years after Trafalgar, when the newly-created Baron Collingwood became virtual Viceroy of the Mediterranean were, as the historian Piers Mackesy put it, 'not of battle. The fights were small, fierce encounters of sloops and gunboats,

cutting-out expeditions, attacks on batteries. Only once did the enemy come out in force. Yet the scale was heroic; and over the vast canvas towers the figure of Collingwood.'

His management of delicate diplomatic rela-tions binding fragile alliances of deys, beys, pashas, emperors, kings and queens was extraordinarily sure-footed. He pre-vented the French fleet from hold-ing any part of the Mediterranean. His conduct in exploiting the Spanish anti-French uprising of May 1808 paved the way for Wellington's ultimately suc-cessful Peninsular campaign. By the time that he died, at sea on March 7th 1810 on his way home from Menorca, he had ensured final British victory at sea against the French not by winning bat-tles, but by preventing them.

That Collingwood gave his entire professional life for his country in the hope of eventual peace says much about the time in which he lived and even more about his personal qualities. That he never saw England or his wife and chil-dren for the last seven years of his life is a tragedy. That he has spent the last 200 years almost entirely neglected, overshadowed by the exploits of his brilliant but flawed friend Nelson, is a histor-ical injustice which his bicentenary ought, finally, to redress.

~ *Max Adams*

Max Adams's biography 'Admiral Collingwood, Nelson's own hero' (Weidenfeld & Nicholson 2005) was written as a result of a Winston Churchill Fellowship enabling him to research and travel in Collingwood's wake.

A bicentenary edition of his book, 'Collingwood, North-umberland's Heart of Oak' is now available from New-castle Libraries, Tyne Bridge Publishing.

~ COLLINGWOOD AT TRAFALGAR ~

COLLINGWOOD, as Nelson's second-in-command, led one of the two columns that struck the line of the Franco-Spanish Combined Fleet shortly after midday on 21 October 1805. The aim was to engage and defeat the enemy rear while Nelson went for the enemy fleet flagship and his squadron occupied the attention of the Combined Fleet's van and centre. Collingwood's flagship was the first to be engaged as HMS *Royal Sovereign,* with a new copper bottom, was fast and pulled ahead of the ships following. She aimed to cut in between the Spanish *Santa Anna,* flagship of the rearward enemy squadron, and the French *Fougeux.*

The latter ships tried to shut *Royal Sovereign* out but Collingwood was not to be denied and ordered *Royal Sovereign* to sail straight at *Fougueux's* bowsprit forcing the latter to turn to starboard, and allowing a raking shot along the full length of the Spanish flagship before loosing a broadside against the Frenchman to starboard. Great damage was done to both ships and their crews but both continued to fight. Four more enemy warships joined in before being diverted by other threats as the rest of the fleet came up. *Royal Sovereign's* yardarms became entangled with those of the *Santa Anna* as the great three-deckers poured shot into each other.

Through the inferno Collingwood remained apparently unperturbed, pacing up and down, eating an apple, even as the flagship's master was killed by a cannon ball beside him and Collingwood suffered very bad bruising in the leg from a flying splinter of wood as well as being hurt in the back by a ball passing by literally too close for comfort. In a world of inaccurate smooth bore weapons injury or death was a matter of chance. The odds favoured the British second-in-command that day, not the fleet commander.

Although the Spanish in *Santa Anna* fought well that day killing 47 men of *Royal Sovereign's* complement and wounding twice as many, the Spanish ship lost almost as many men again as superior British rates of fire told their usual terrible story.

As her fire slackened it looked as if *Santa Anna* had surrendered but she made a last attempt to get away moving ahead of *Royal Sovereign* and raking her before being re-engaged by the British ship's starboard guns. Then two of *Santa Anna's* weakened masts fell and she finally struck

(Courtesy: Susan Collingwood-Cameron)

A detail from 'The Storm after the Battle of Trafalgar' attributed to J. W. Carmichael.

her colours at 2.20. As she did so *Royal Sovereign* lost her mainmast also.

Now a boat arrived from HMS *Victory*. Lieutenant Alexander Hills came on board to inform the second-in-command that Nelson had been wounded. Collingwood sensed from Hills' expression that the situation was very serious. He now ordered the frigate *Euryalus* to take *Royal Sovereign* in tow and the frigate's distinguished Captain Blackwood was sent on board *Santa Anna* to bring its admiral, Alava, on board. The latter had been seriously wounded in the head and sent his flag captain with his sword. Collingwood sent the captain back to look after his admiral.

As the ships that had originally led the enemy fleet came round to attempt to rescue the centre and rear, Collingwood drove them away, engaging them under tow until enemy fire broke the cable, while ordering the after-most ships in his squadron to see them off. Blackwood now closed *Victory* to hear the news of Nelson's death. He then took Captain Hardy to meet Collingwood and surrender Nelson's command to him.

Hardy told Collingwood that Nelson had ordered the fleet and its captures to go to anchor but Collingwood disagreed. Instead, shifting his flag to *Euryalus* which again took *Royal Sovereign* in tow, he ordered his ships to make towards Gibraltar, disabled ships to be towed. Now Collingwood's luck finally ran out. Worsening weather caused *Euryalus* and *Royal Sovereign* to collide and Collingwood belatedly ordered the crippled fleet to anchor. The storm struck in full force on the 22nd and lasted on and off for four days. In the terrible conditions Collingwood set about destroying the prizes, some of which also sank, made their escape or were recaptured (among them the *Santa Anna*), leaving only four out of the original 17 captured ships in British hands. Collingwood's decision-making caused controversy both at the time and since.

Nevertheless Collingwood remained sufficiently trusted by the Admiralty and the British Government as a whole to remain to be worked to death over the next four and a half years as C-in-C of the Mediterranean Fleet. His central involvement in the overall destruction of the Franco-Spanish fleet at Trafalgar overshadowed his losses in the storm and he emerged from the battle as Baron Collingwood, its other, but still living hero.

~ Eric Grove

Dr Grove is Professor of Naval History at the University of Salford. A prolific author who frequently appears on radio and television, he is a Vice President of the Society for Nautical Research, a Member of Council of the Royal Navy Records Society and a Fellow of the Royal Historical Society.

THE VICTORY SLIPSONG

YE true Sons of Britain give ear to ditty, a matchless story I mean to relate,
Concerning Lord Nelson's glorious victory, and how unfortunately he met with his fate.
His number it was about forty-four thousand, the choicest of seamen both loyal and good,
And at their head a valiant commander, an undaunted hero called Lord Collingwood.
He cries to both Captains and Seamen, stand stout to your posts, be loyal and true,
The French fleets approaching, we'll make them surrender, Old England my boys depends upon you.
As his lordship on deck the last orders gave, from the end of a section he received a ball,
Under his left breast he was mortally wounded which occasioned his lordship's downfall.

As his lordship lay bleeding, he cries my dear Collingwood, tell me, kind sir, how the battle does go?
The action is ours, my lord, he replied, our enemy has got a complete overthrow –
The great Trinidad we sunk to the bottom, eighteen we have captured & have them in tow.
Let the sacred name of JEHOVAH be praised, since fortune this day has been to us good,
My blessing I leave with my noble seamen, my post I resign to you Lord Collingwood.
The world never bred such two gallant Commanders, commanding together, till Nelson did fall,
But now in one grave those 2 worthies remain, in the grand Cathedral church of St. Paul.

Slipsong, published circa 1810

SLIPSONGS were the simplest of printed ballads, quickly and cheaply produced. Itinerant ballad-sellers hawked them on the street corner to cater to a popular market eager for news fresh off the press.

What at first sight appears to be a jolly piece of patriotic doggerel soon takes on a surprising tone with an overtly religious tenor recurrent throughout the piece.

However, of more particular interest to the current reader is the direct link that is made between Nelson and 'a valiant commander, an undaunted hero called Lord Collingwood'. This is most notable in the midst of the piece when as Nelson lies dying, he calls for news of the action. Not Hardy but Collingwood comes to his side.

This distortion of the facts was bolstered by sound commercial sense, as, doubtless the prominent inclusion of Nelson's name was guaranteed to improve sales.

Cuthbert Collingwood's naval career was in many ways dazzled by Nelson's brilliance.

But at Trafalgar as he led *Royal Sovereign* belching smoke and fire through the line of the Combined Fleets the nobility of the fellow showed to the full. How fitting then, the author of these verses should choose that event to remember these 'two gallant Commanders', who in death lie side by side in St Paul's, Nelson in his magnificent sarcophagus, Collingwood in his plain tomb; both beneath the same dome.

~ Anthony Cross and Horatio Blood

~ THE TARS OF THE TYNE ~

AT the end of the 18th century, as Collingwood's naval career entered its most successful phase, the seafaring communities of the North East contained one of the largest concentrations of skilled mariners anywhere in the United Kingdom. These seamen manned the colliers, Baltic traders and Greenland whalers based in the ports of the region and they became prime targets for the press gangs of Newcastle, Shields and Sunderland after 1793.

When the French Wars ended in 1815 thousands of local men, or at least those who survived the experience, had served in the wooden walls of Nelson's navy. Some like William Hall, who fought at the eleventh gun in *Victory*, William Gardner in *Colossus* and Henry Potts in *Dreadnought,* were Trafalgar veterans who lived long enough to claim their campaign medals in 1848. Potts was badly wounded and had his left leg amputated below the knee.

A contemporary observer recalled many of them as old men hanging around the quays, wharves and ferry landings of Shields... 'in every stage of picturesque dismemberment — one arm, one leg, one arm and one leg — hardy, patient, long-suffering fellows whose bronzed faces showed in every line of hardship and privation.' They were the surviving representatives of Collingwood's 'Tars of the Tyne' who fought with distinction at every major naval engagement of the Napoleonic era. Hundreds fought at Trafalgar, many of them forcibly recruited from laden colliers arriving in the Thames during the 'hot press' of 1803.

George Irwin, a seaman from Hexham who later wrote an account of his seafaring career, narrowly escaped impressments from the collier *Hercules,* in-bound from Shields, anchored at Woolwich awaiting her turn to discharge her coal. Dozens of others were less fortunate and many were subsequently drafted to *Colossus*, a new ship fitting out at Deptford. Robert Jackson, a 21-year-old able seaman from South Shields, Benjamin Hopper, aged 30 from Etal in Northumberland and Hardin Hall from Sunderland, aged 45, were all pressed in the Thames that night. Most of the others joined the ship in August from *Zealand* at The Nore. They included at least seven of the 53 keelmen controversially pressed on the Tyne a few months before.

Colossus was pre-eminently the 'Geordie' ship at Trafalgar and eventually claimed the dubious distinction of suffering the highest casualties of any ship in Nelson's fleet that day — 40 killed and 160 wounded. *Colossus* entered the battle almost an hour after Collingwood's flagship, *Royal Sovereign,* and was soon engaged on both sides. Jackson later recalled... 'We ran the muzzles of our lower deck guns close against their side and so blazed away. Nothing could be heard for two hours but thundering and cheering.' He was fortunate to survive the battle unscathed and returned to the familiar collier brigs of the coal trade when the war ended although he does not seem to have lived long enough to claim his Trafalgar medal.

Of course, not all seamen were impressed like Jackson. More than half of the Tyneside Tars who served at Trafalgar were volunteers and many of them joined the Royal Navy on the understanding that they would be allowed to serve under particular officers like Collingwood. His well-known preference for officers and men from Tyneside made him a popular choice for local seamen. In May

Hundreds of Tyneside Tars were pressed from colliers arriving in the Thames and forced to serve on warships like this which carried crews of 500-600 men.

1793, for example, soon after Britain entered the French Revolutionary War, Collingwood wrote to the Admiralty... 'being particularly connected at Newcastle I engaged my friends there to use their influence with the seamen and near 50 men were entered.'

He went on to express his concern that only three had been permitted to join him and enclosed a letter from the men observing that... 'from certain appearances it seems as if they mean to put us aboard other ships and as we entered for you could wish to be there as soon as possible.' The problem for Collingwood was that he often moved from ship to ship and it was impractical for the Admiralty to permit more than a handful of petty officers to move with him, particularly since prime seamen were in high demand everywhere in the Navy. Ten years later in September 1803 Collingwood, by then a rear-admiral, received over 200 'Newcastle volunteers' into his flagship *Venerable* but few of them remained with him for long, the majority, including some of the keelmen, remained with *Prince* and fought the guns of that ship at Trafalgar.

Collingwood's officers fared rather better because of the practice of taking his senior officer with him when he moved from ship to ship. When Collingwood received his 'Newcastle volunteers' he also acknowledged the arrival of 'two youngsters' just setting out on their naval careers; 15-year-old Granville Thompson from Newcastle and George Castle from Durham who was 13. Both of the boys were rated midshipmen and both of them fought in *Royal Sovereign* at Trafalgar.

Thompson was wounded but Castle came through the battle unscathed and left a graphic account of his experience in a letter to his sister addressed from Gibraltar... 'We were alongside a great three-decker... and I stuck so close to one gun it was impossible to miss her... she was a Spanish Admiral's ship. I looked once out of our stern ports — but I saw nothing but French and Spaniards all around firing at us in all directions.' Castle also described the gory consequences of close-quarters fighting... 'It was shocking to see many brave seamen mangled so, some with their heads half shot away, others with their entrails mashed lying panting upon the deck. The greatest slaughter was upon the quarterdeck and the poop.'

Within half an hour Collingwood and his flag-captain Edward Rotheram were the only unwounded officers left on the quarterdeck. Rotheram was born at Hexham but had lived in Newcastle since he was a boy. He joined Collingwood on *Dreadnought* in 1804 but did not enjoy the Admiral's confidence and the relationship between them was difficult. 'I have a gentleman from Newcastle for my captain,' he wrote to his cousin Edward Collingwood a month before Trafalgar, 'but he has no talent as a sea officer and is of very little assistance to me'.

Collingwood found Rotheram's abrasive manner and limited abilities of command particularly irritating although he was soon to discover that these shortcomings were, to an extent, offset by Rotheram's undoubted bravery and courage under fire. Early in the battle when a junior officer advised that Rotheram should make himself a less conspicuous target for Spanish musketry by removing his distinctive gold-laced hat, he replied indignantly... 'I have always fought in a cocked hat and I always will.' Collingwood clearly approved of these sentiments, commending the bravery of officers and men in his famous Trafalgar Dispatch.

A few days after the battle he wrote privately to his sister... 'Tell Thompson's father that his son behaved admirably in the battle and that if he had served his time I would have made him a lieutenant the same day.' Thompson was still only 17. He was eventually promoted to lieutenant by Collingwood in 1809 after further distinguishing himself in numerous smaller actions and boat attacks. He returned briefly to Newcastle in 1812 where he sat for the portrait now in the collection of the Laing Art Gallery. Thompson eventually rose to become the first lieutenant of a frigate but died of yellow fever in the Bahamas in 1817.

The other 'youngster', George Castle, became a lieutenant in 1811 and saw much action in the Mediterranean and the West Indies before the Napoleonic War ended in 1815.

Collingwood's Midshipman, Granville Thompson (1788-1817).

(Courtesy: Laing Art Gallery)

He died in 1826 the same year as another of Collingwood's Northumbrians, Commander William Landless. After Trafalgar, Collingwood had him promoted and commissioned to a sloop of war. In December 1806, sailing from Gibraltar and operating against French and Spanish commerce, Landless captured a small merchant ship laden with cochineal and indigo. It proved to be such a valuable prize that Landless was able to end his seagoing career, buy a farm at Easington near Belford and live in comfortable retirement.

Post-war life for Collingwood's 'Tars of the Tyne' was very different. For many of them the French Wars ended as they had begun, with strikes and trade disputes about wages and conditions in the coal trade. Few left any permanent record of their naval service although a rare survival from the 1840s, two annual reports of a Victorian maritime charity, The Tyne Aged Sailors and Scullermen's Society, offers historians a glimpse of their lives.

The Society owned 14 small rowing boats which it leased to aged mariners for sixpence a week. The boats were used to ferry passengers across the river and provided a modest income for the old men. All of them had served in the Navy in their prime. Boat number 5 was leased to James Donnison, aged 68, who spent 50 years at sea. He became a victim of the press gang in 1793 and served under Nelson in *Agamemnon* in 1795. Boat number 11 was leased to William Sim, aged 63, who was also impressed and served in *Orion* at Trafalgar. He was subsequently awarded £10 in compensation for wounds he received at the battle. He died in the

'*The sons of Tyne, in seas of blood, Trafalgar's fight did join,*
When led by dauntless Collingwood, The hero of the Tyne'.

From the song Coaly Tyne, author unknown

~

workhouse at Tynemouth about 1860.

~ *Tony Barrow*

On May 1-2 Newcastle Arts Centre and Trinity House Newcastle host '*The Life and Times of Admiral Collingwood'*, a 2 day North-East Centre for Lifelong Learning workshop. For more details, see page 32, Festival Programme.

Tony Barrow has an M.Ed from Newcastle University and a Ph.D from Northumbria University for research into the whaling trade of North East England later published as a book with that title by Sunderland University Press (2001). Head of History & Archaeology at Newcastle College until he retired in 2007, he now teaches part-time for Sunderland University's Centre for Lifelong Learning on aspects of the maritime history of the region.

His new book 'Collingwood's Northumbrians', a companion volume to 'Trafalgar Geordies' (2005) has just been published.

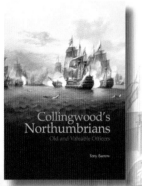
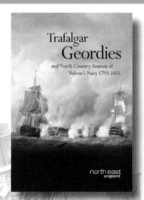

~ TRAFALGAR MEMORIAL IN SUNDERLAND ~

WITH the possible exception of the "new towns" constructed since the Second World War, it is unusual to find a town or village in the United Kingdom which does not have a memorial to those who lost their lives in conflicts past. It is rare, however, to find a memorial to a group of men who participated, without necessarily losing their lives, in a single battle, and a sea battle at that.

Yet this year, in the part of the city of Sunderland known as "Old Sunderland", that is exactly what will happen. A memorial, listing the names of the seamen from that specific area who were at the battle of Trafalgar, will be unveiled. To be fair, the existence of this brave group of men has never been forgotten locally, mainly because of the existence of Trafalgar Square, a set of houses built (and

HMS *Victory*. King was in fact, one of three of this group who were actually killed in action during the battle; a further two were wounded and one died of his injuries shortly after the battle. In addition, William Featherstonehaugh, a 49-year-old Quartermaster on the famous HMS ("Fighting") *Temeraire*, who must have been delighted when he was ordered to transfer to a French prize, the *Fougueux*, with orders to take her to England, was drowned when the vessel ran aground and broke up on the night of the 23rd October.

Just six of the Old Sunderland men received the Naval General Service Medal with Trafalgar Clasp, commonly referred to today as 'the Trafalgar Medal'. However, as this medal was not made available until 1848, some 43 years after the battle and could only be awarded to a living sur-

The grounds of Trafalgar Square Homes

still run today) by a charity called the Sunderland Aged Seamen's Homes. These historic and picturesque almshouses were built in 1840 — some five years before the square of the same name was completed in London — in honour of the Sunderland men at the battle. Yet those names have never been on public display. Between them, they were serving on 28 of the English ships at Trafalgar; a number were on board Collingwood's ship, HMS *Royal Sovereign*, and it is therefore quite fitting that that this tribute will take place in 2010 and form part of the Collingwood 2010 Festival.

The monument will be erected in the grounds of the Trafalgar Square Homes, but will, for the most part, be accessible to the public. It will take the form of a tablet of blue-grey marble with gold lettering, listing the men, their ages, ranks and the ships on which they served and will be set at an angle, tilted towards the flag-staff that stands in one corner of the Square.

The youngest of the Old Sunderland contingent was 14-year old Thomas Brown on board HMS *Minotaur* and the oldest 56-year old Quartermaster John King on board

vivor, or the relatives of those who died after June 1847, and additionally that applications closed in 1851, this low number is of little real surprise.

Today, Old Sunderland is just a part of a relatively new City, but there are those who still recognise it as a distinct and defined area and remember when a man would 'not cross the boundary to drink in an adjacent part of the town'. There are those too, committed to preserving its heritage before it disappears or is swallowed up in a wider archive. Interestingly, Trafalgar Square lies but a stone's throw from the grave of Jack Crawford, who was reputed to have climbed the mast of HMS *Venerable* at the Battle of Camperdown to nail Admiral Duncan's colour to the mast top... but that is another story.

~ *Stephen Healy*

Captain Healy is a trustee of the Sunderland Aged Seamen's Homes and chairman of the Collingwood 2010 Festival Committee.

~ HMS ROYAL SOVEREIGN ~

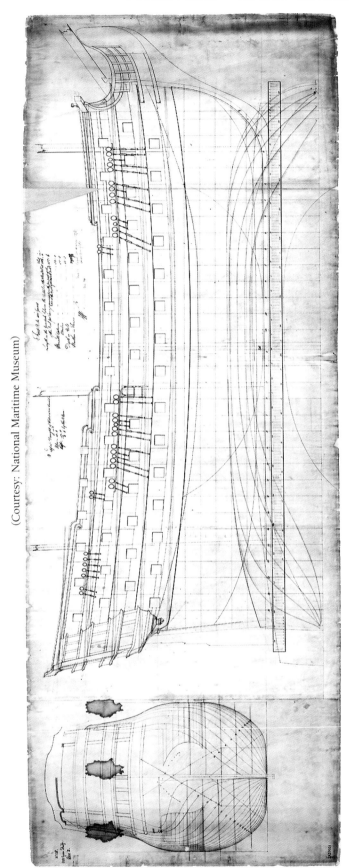

One of the plans used during the construction of HMS Royal Sovereign.

Flagship of Vice Admiral Collingwood
at the Battle of Trafalgar

Built: Plymouth Dockyard
Keel laid: 7th January 1774
Launched: 11th September 1786

Principal battle honours:
   The Glorious First of June
   The Battle of Trafalgar

Subsequent service:
   Retired to harbour service
   1826, re-named HMS *Captain*

Fate: Broken up 1841

Class / type: 100-gun, 1st rate,
                        ship of the line
Weight: 2175 tons (2210 tonnes)
Length: 183 feet 10$\frac{1}{2}$ inches
                        (56 metres)
Beam: 52 feet 1 inch (15.9 metres)

Armament: 100 guns:
                        – Gundeck: 28 x 32 pdrs
                        – Middle gundeck:
                        28 x 24 pdrs
                        – Upper gundeck:
                        30 x 12 pdrs
                        – Quarterdeck: 10 x 12 pdrs
                        – Forecastle: 4 x 12 pdrs

Complement: 835

~ THE BOAST OF OLD NORTHUMBERLAND: COLLINGWOOD AND THE 1805 CLUB ~

When Nelson sailed for Trafalgar
With all his country's best,
He held them dear as brothers are,
But one beyond the rest.
For when the fleet with heroes manned
To clear the decks began,
The boast of old Northumberland
He sent to lead the Van.

Sir Henry Newbolt

TWO hundred years ago a very weary 61-year-old sailor suffering from serious strains to both health and happiness prepared to come home. He had been away for six long years, five of them in command of the prestigious Mediterranean Fleet supporting the military campaign against Napoleon in the Iberian Peninsula. He had had a

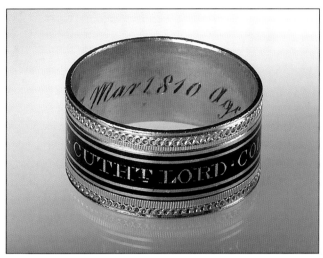

leading role off Cape Trafalgar on 21 October 1805, which secures his fame, but it is only recently that Vice-Admiral Collingwood, Baron of Caldburne and Hethpool, has emerged from under the shadow cast by the great Nelson, allowing us to recognise his distinctive talents and the significance of his naval career as a whole.

'See how that noble fellow Collingwood takes his ship into action!' remarked Nelson to Captain Henry Blackwood. The *Royal Sovereign* leading the Lee Division was bearing down on the rear of the Combined Fleet engaging the enemy at least 15 minutes before any other British ship. As a midshipman observing him more closely recollected, 'I see before me dear old Cuddy (as Collingwood was affectionately known) walking the break of the poop, with his little triangular gold-laced cocked hat, tight silk stockings, and buckles, musing over the

progress of the fight and munching an apple.' Collingwood was pleased with himself. 'Oh Rotherham, he exclaimed to the *Royal Sovereign's* captain, 'what would Nelson give to be here!'

The Combined Fleet was annihilated but, in his own words, Collingwood's mind was distracted

Memorabilia commemorating Collingwood's death – bracelet, mourning ring and mug.

(Courtesy: National Maritime Museum)

by 'The ever-to-be-lamented death of Vice Admiral Lord Viscount Nelson, who, in the late conflict with the enemy, fell in the hour of victory...'

Separated from his friend by death and his family by duty, Collingwood's next five years in the Mediterranean are now seen as a

culmination of an active and successful career, which revealed his mastery of strategy and diplomacy and his instinctive judgement when dealing with foreign affairs. His strategic vision and understanding of the region, including the importance of North Africa, became the very essence of British government policy. British ministers and the Admiralty held him in such high esteem that they kept him on station and refused his requests for leave, until he was 'so weak that application to business [was] impossible'.

In the words of veteran historian, Piers Mackesy, 'The scale [of the Mediterranean theatre] was heroic, and over the vast canvas towers the figure of Collingwood.' Few men have risen to such eminence while being so long out of the public eye.

It is wretched that this honest and sentimental man not only lost his closest friend but also never returned to England to see his wife and daughters, nor his beloved garden in Morpeth. Dying within four days of at last receiving orders to return, his body was brought to England and buried close to Nelson's in a plain, unadorned box tomb in the crypt of St Paul's Cathedral.

These facts highlight Collingwood's significance to The 1805 Club, a charity concerned with the often forgotten monuments, graves and memorials of those who served in the eighteenth century sailing navy. Where Nelson has become the icon for the ethos of the Royal Navy and Britain's maritime history, Collingwood is symbolic of the tens of thousands of sailors who took part, yet have been eclipsed by the more famous sailors of the era: Anson, Rodney, Cook, Boscawen, Hawke, and ultimately Nelson.

The force of nature is a constant challenge to the preservation of these monuments and memorials. Stones crack and mosses creep, roots pry into fissures and acid rain dissolves. The Club's conservation work seeks to slow down this process of decay so that all can enjoy, and more importantly learn from, the wonderful tales associated with those memorialised as we seek to bring them 'alive' through original research and with imaginative events.

The 1805 Club is therefore very proud to have initiated the *Collingwood 2010 Festival:* the last great naval bicentenary of the Napoleonic period. It is heartening that Northumberland has risen to the occasion and continues to boast his name.

~ Peter Warwick

Peter Warwick is Chairman of The 1805 Club and author of 'Voices from the Battle of Trafalgar' *(David & Charles 2005). Details of The 1805 Club can be found at www.1805club.org*

THE 1805 CLUB
Conserving memorials to Georgian naval heroes

THE 1805 Club is proud to have initiated the *Collingwood 2010 Festival,* celebrating the last great naval bicentenary of the Napoleonic period, and wishes it every success.

The club, a registered charity, is dedicated to preserving the historic environment of the Georgian sailing navy, as represented by its monuments, graves and memorials. No other organisation exists specifically to conserve these monuments and memorials, which are the touching reminders of individual and personal bravery, adventure and achievement across the multitude of oceans in terms of seamanship, exploration and war, which helped to both shape the world and form our understanding of it. Vice-Admiral Lord Collingwood is one of the better known heroes of this age and his tomb and memorials are well-preserved. Others are not.

Our mission is to identify and conserve these graves and memorials so that we can all learn from the wonderful tales associated with those memorialised as we seek to bring them 'alive' through original research and with imaginative and exciting events. The 1805 Club has undertaken more than 40 conservation projects since it was founded 20 years ago, funded largely through grants from charitable trusts.

The Club also publishes the *Trafalgar Chronicle,* which is recognised as a major source of new research about the Georgian sailing navy, and a lively newsletter, the Kedge Anchor. We foster close links with the Royal Navy and run an ambitious events programme. You can find out more about our work and the benefits of membership at: www.1805club.org

The 1805 Club

THE DRAPERS' COMPANY

THE Drapers' Company received its first royal charter in 1364 and was incorporated in 1438, making it one of the earliest of the City of London's trade guilds.

From its origins it was a benevolent institution, helping its members who fell into distress and that role is reflected today in the administration of nine Charitable Trusts and three almshouse charities. The Company also continues to play a role in the life of the City: its Liverymen carry out important functions in the elections of the government of the City of London and certain of its officers.

Vice Admiral Cuthbert

Collingwood was awarded the Freedom of the Drapers' Company in December 1805, joining his colleague and friend Vice Admiral Horatio Nelson within its ranks. Captain Thomas Masterman Hardy was another participant of the Battle of Trafalgar to later receive this honour.

The Drapers' Company is pleased to support the Collingwood 2010 Festival in recognition of a group of naval heroes that define a period in English history and in this, the 200th anniversary of his death, Vice Admiral Lord Collingwood in particular.

~ COLLINGWOOD –
A NORTHUMBRIAN ABROAD ~

An exhibition at the Discovery Museum, Newcastle upon Tyne, open until June 27, 2010.

WHEN Admiral Lord Collingwood died at sea on March 7, 1810 on board his flagship, *Ville de Paris*, he was more than 1,000 miles from his native Northumberland, but he had done his duty to the very end.

This exhibition marks the 200th anniversary of Collingwood's death using an interesting mix of items from Tyne and Wear Archives and Museums collections together with loans from descendants of Admiral Collingwood and others to commemorate his life and extraordinary naval service. A full length portrait of Collingwood from the Laing Art Gallery painted in 1806 by James Lonsdale was too big to fit the exhibition space so it will take pride of place alongside *Turbinia* in the Discovery entrance.

One of the items on loan from the Collingwood family is a log book he kept when he was a midshipman aboard the 28-gun frigate *Liverpool* on a voyage to the Mediterranean in 1770-71. Although still a midshipman he was rated master's mate, with special responsibility for navigation, and the book includes drawings of distinctive coastlines and a plan of Port Mahon in Menorca.

Another star loan item is the sword Collingwood received to signify the surrender of *Santa Anna*, the Spanish flagship at Trafalgar. He was told it belonged to Vice-Admiral d'Alava and that d'Alava was not expected to live. Collingwood allowed the 'dying' man to stay aboard *Santa Anna* which drifted into

An 1806 portrait of Collingwood wearing the regulation dress uniform of a Vice Admiral painted by James Lonsdale.

(Courtesy: Laing Art Gallery)

Cadiz and d'Alava recovered from his wounds. He later denied he had surrendered because it wasn't his sword that was handed over! Collingwood had cause to regret his humane treatment of the Spanish admiral since he had lost a valuable prize.

The exhibition looks at Collingwood's naval service but also tries to show how he used letters to maintain ties with family and friends back in Northumberland. Extracts from these letters are used throughout.

Collingwood was happiest at home in Morpeth, enjoying family life and pursuing his hobby of gardening. The tragic irony is that once he joined the navy he was able to spend only seven of the remaining 49 years of his life in his beloved Northumberland.

~ *Ian Whitehead, Tyne and Wear Museums*

'Sea Piece with British Men-of-War' by Nicholas Pocock (1740-1821). This painting shows frigates probably at the Downs anchorage, off the east coast of Kent. Collingwood was promoted post-captain to the 28-gun frigate Hinchinbrooke in 1780. He replaced his friend Horatio Nelson who had been sent home from England to recover from illness.

~ THE COLLINGWOOD 2010 FESTIVAL LOGO ~

THE Collingwood 2010 Festival image, developed by RE Media of Gateshead, is intended to work on a number of levels.

First of all, particularly to residents of the North East, it is a reproduction of the iconic monument at Tynemouth, complete with cannon, which overlooks the entrance to the River Tyne.

Secondly, notwithstanding that the festival is an opportunity to redress the balance, it is representative of the fact that history has continued to portray Collingwood in the shadow of Nelson.

Thirdly, it recalls a little known piece of fun between the two men. They met as lieutenants serving in the West Indies and became firm friends for life. In 1784, at a party held by Mrs Mary Moutray, friend and confidante of both, Nelson and Collingwood decided to draw each other.

Collingwood's image of Nelson was drawn first and Mrs Moutray recorded: 'When the laughter which this created was over, Captain Nelson said, "And now, Collingwood, in revenge I will draw you in that queue (hair-piece) of yours", and produced in his turn an outline drawing in which he has caught with considerable success the features of his friend.' Although there is some tone to the picture, it is in effect, a silhouette, as is the technique employed in the logo.

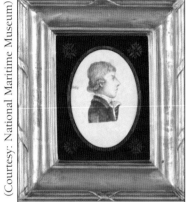

(Courtesy: National Maritime Museum)

Collingwood's Antigua drawing of Nelson who was wearing a wig to cover his head shaved after a bout of fever.

COLLINGWOOD 2010

(Courtesy: National Maritime Museum)

Lieutenant Collingwood drawn by Nelson in Antigua, 1784.

THE NELSON SOCIETY

THIS society exists specifically to promote interest in the life and character of Vice-Admiral Horatio Nelson. It is, however, entirely proper and correct that we acknowledge his great friend and colleague Vice-Admiral Cuthbert Collingwood and the Society is pleased to be doing so this year by holding its Annual General Meeting in the North East of England over the Trafalgar Day weekend in October. Our event will coincide with the official close of the Collingwood 2010 Festival and our members are both honoured to be involved and very much looking forward to visiting the region.

There have been many books and articles written about the relationship between Nelson and Collingwood and it is apparent from them all that the respect and admiration they had for each other continued to develop throughout their lives. The affection that Collingwood had for Nelson is never more demonstrated than in the opening words of a General Order issued by him to the Officers commanding the ships of the Fleet on the day following the battle, in which he states:

"The ever-to-be-lamented death of Lord Viscount Nelson... who fell in the action of the twenty-first, in the arms of victory, covered with glory; whose memory will be ever dear to the British Navy, and the British Nation; whose zeal for the honour of his King, and for the interests of his Country, will be ever held up as a shining example for a British Seaman".

His report to the Admiralty, written the same day and contained in a document now generally referred to as the 'Trafalgar Dispatch' went further. "My heart is rent with the most poignant grief for the death of a friend, to whom I was bound by the strongest ties of affection".

The Collingwood 2010 Festival is an opportunity for the Nelson Society to join with our sister organisation, the 1805 Club, and with the people of the North East, in celebrating the life and memory of Vice-Admiral Cuthbert Collingwood and for our members in particular to explore the relationship between Nelson and the man who undoubtedly (and rightly so) is a hero in the North East.

The Nelson Society is registered in England & Wales as charity number 296979.

For more information, please visit our website at www.nelson-society.com

~ THE COLLINGWOOD FAMILY ~

I HAD always been aware that my great-great-great-great uncle Cuthbert had been Admiral Lord Collingwood, Nelson's second-in-command at the Battle of Trafalgar. However, I am rather ashamed to admit that my knowledge of the Admiral did not extend much further than the bare facts.

This all rather changed in 2005 when the "forgotten hero" was again brought into the limelight largely due to the efforts of his biographer, Max Adams. My mother, Susan Collingwood-Cameron, was able to assist Max with his work by providing access to various documents and artefacts which are still in the family's possession. This naturally increased our curiosity, which turned to necessity as 2005 approached when we were asked to participate in various events and some knowledge of the subject was naturally expected!

An increased knowledge of the life and deeds of the Admiral was not the only benefit of 2005 that came our way. The raised profile of Collingwood led to us establishing contact with his direct descendants, some of whom we were aware of and some of whom we weren't.

Our branch of the Collingwood family is descended from the Admiral's younger brother, John Collingwood. Our direct family tree was relatively simple and well known. This was not the case with the Admiral's direct descendants. The Admiral fathered two daughters: Sarah and Mary Patience. Their husbands were not agin adopting the name Collingwood, which complicates matters although it is a habit which is not exclusive to that side of the family! Furthermore, some descendants ended up in Ireland where many family records were lost to posterity as they were torched during the troubles.

Sarah, the elder daughter, married George Newnham, who changed his name to Collingwood and wrote a biography of the Admiral in 1828. It went to five editions and radically changed his country's perceptions of the man. They also had two daughters. The elder never married but the younger, called Sarah, married firstly Cuthbert Collingwood Hall and then John Howell but died without issue.

Susan Collingwood-Cameron, the Admirals' great-great-great neice at the opening of the Discovery Museum Collingwood 2010 Exhibition.

~

"I have no desire to command in any port, except at Morpeth, where I am only second."
(Collingwood to Dr Alexander Carlyle – April 1799)

~

Collingwood's great-great-great granddaughter, Heather McKinlay and Susan Collingwood-Cameron with the Admiral's night glass.

The Hall family changed its name to Fitzwilliams in 1849 and we are now in touch with members of the family who are based in west Wales and possess various Collingwood artefacts, which presumably originated from this marriage.

Mary Patience married Anthony Denny and produced four children, three of whom went on to produce children of their own. Two direct descendants from their oldest child, Anthony, are Nicholas Collingwood DuSautoy and his sister, Carmen. We are in regular contact with them both and Nicholas has been able to attend various Collingwood-related events in the North East.

A new relative appeared recently in the form of Heather McKinlay who currently resides in Dubai. She is also a direct descendant of Mary Patience, via Anthony. His daughter, also Sarah, married Col Thomas Bradell of County Wexford. Many of the records pertaining to this element of the family were destroyed, so meeting Heather was an unexpected pleasure.

In 2010 the family has much to look forward to as the life and deeds of Admiral Lord Collingwood are celebrated in a number of events to mark the bicentenary of his death. In doing so, I hope that more bona fide descendants will emerge from the broad unknown and so provide further pieces of the Collingwood family jigsaw.

~ *Angus Collingwood-Cameron*

~ COLLINGWOOD: A FATHER FIGURE ~

CUTHBERT Collingwood and his ships were legendary for their fighting expertise. The Royal Navy would later name its gunnery school at Portsmouth HMS *Excellent* in honour of Collingwood's skill in battle. Yet, in spite of his warrior reputation, the Tyneside admiral was by nature a compassionate man who cared deeply about the welfare of his men.

Collingwood disliked the ritualistic public floggings that were rife in the Navy and his logbooks testify that he was more lenient than most commanders. He was a strict disciplinarian who was appreciated by his men for his sense of justice and fairness. A serving crewman wrote that:

> "Captain Collingwood visited his men daily when they were sick and gave them food from his table. Sailors called him 'father' and when they changed ships, many men were seen in tears at their departure."

His paternal authority was very effective at sea but in his own family he was very much an absent father. He married Sarah Blackett in 1791 and in two short years they produced two daughters before he was called away for another ten years of continuous service. In May 1802, he returned to the Morpeth family home for a solitary year and spent time with his daughters Sarah junior, now aged 9, and Mary Patience, aged 8. It was the happiest time of his life and the thought of coming home to his beloved 'darlings' always sustained him when he was in foreign waters.

Collingwood wrote home continuously and did his best to educate his daughters from a distance. He was a fervent Tynesider but he saw the disadvantage of a strong regional accent, which he felt might make his children appear uncouth. He told his wife:

> "However, their hearts and their minds are of much more consequence than their tongues. As for learning, I would like the girls to be taught mathematics and geometry — of all sciences in the world these are the most entertaining. Also astronomy to give them an idea of the beauty and wonder of creation…"

Collingwood encouraged his wife to see that their daughter Sarah learnt French although his observation on the Gallic nation was caustic:

> "The language is the only thing French she need possess for there is very little else from that country which I should wish her to love or imitate."

He was anxious that they should not waste time on frivolity:

> "Above all things, keep novels out of their reach. They are corrupters of tender minds… novels turn their heads before they are enabled to distinguish truth from these fictions which are devised merely for entertainment. When they have passed their climacteric it will be time enough to begin novels."

Sarah Collingwood.
This miniature might have accompanied Collingwood on his many voyages.
(Courtesy: Susan Collingwood-Cameron)

A 'climacteric', according to the OED is a 'period of life when fertility and sexual activity are in decline' in other words, when they are old maids!

In Cuthbert's letter dated 5th April 1806 he comments on the family's visit to London where Sarah is to be presented at Court. His daughters are also making the trip and he is anxious that they make the most of the experience:

> "I hope that in this journey the education of our children does not stop; but that, even on the road, they may study the geography of that part of England through which they travel, and keep a regular journal, not of what they eat and drink but of the nature of the country, its appearance, its produce, and some lively description of the manners of the inhabitants. I hope you will take your time in town and show my girls everything curious. I am sure you will visit the tomb of my dear friend."

Collingwood was referring to Nelson's resting place in the crypt of St Paul's Cathedral — a location which would be the Northumbrian's own final resting place. Anticipating the future, Collingwood wrote to a friend:

> "I am delighted with my little daughters, who quite meet my expectations. I doubt not we shall have an inexhaustible source of joy. How thankful I am for such blessings."

It is a poignant message, for after Trafalgar in 1805, Collingwood stayed in command of the fleet at this volatile time until he was too ill to continue. He left from Menorca to return home to Morpeth but sadly after two days, he died at sea and would never see his family again.

~ *Andrew Griffin*

~ COLLINGWOOD AND MORPETH ~

IN 1791, after Cuthbert Collingwood married Sarah Blackett, the daughter of the Mayor of Newcastle, they set up home in Morpeth, first renting then subsequently purchasing a house on Oldgate. This property, now named Collingwood House, is owned by St. Robert's Church and bears a plaque above its door to commemorate its notable former owner.

Collingwood House in Oldgate.

In the grounds of the property there was a riverside path, known as the 'quarter deck', where the admiral could walk up and down in the open, as he would have done on his ship. From a summerhouse, which he called his 'poop deck', after the high exposed deck of a ship, he could view the River Wansbeck when he was home on leave from his naval duties. He loved exploring Morpeth and its environs, and he is believed to have planted hundreds of acorns on the river valley sides to replace oak trees used to build the ships of the Royal Navy.

Collingwood had little aspiration to be seen as a national hero and his love of Morpeth and its peaceful nature is a reflection of this. Although his duties prevented Collingwood from spending much time in the town he felt truly at home there, a feeling that is demonstrated in one of the many letters he wrote to his wife:

> *"Should we decide to change the place of our dwelling…I should be forever regretting those beautiful views which are nowhere to be exceeded…The fact is, whenever I think how I am to be happy again, my thoughts carry me back to Morpeth, where, out of the fuss and parade of the world, surrounded by those I loved most dearly and who loved me, I enjoyed as much happiness as my nature is capable of."*
> (Collingwood, 1806)

Collingwood was at peace in Morpeth, and this is evident through his devotion to his garden. Later, in the same letter, Collingwood asks his wife:

> *"How do the trees which I planted thrive? Is there shade under the three oaks for a comfortable summer seat? Do the poplars grow at the walk, and does the wall of the terrace stand firm?"*

An interpretation board relating to Collingwood's garden and his 'poop deck' was installed across the river from the house, at High Stanners in 2009. Although the summerhouse is now in a dilapidated state, the interpretation board shows an artist's impression of what it may have looked like during Collingwood's lifetime. It is hoped that more research will be conducted which will lead to a full reconstruction of the structure or at the very least, receipt of funding to conserve and make safe such a valuable piece of Morpeth's and Lord Collingwood's heritage.

In October 2005, twelve English oak trees were planted across the river from Collingwood House by pupils from nine Morpeth schools to commemorate the 200th anniversary of the Battle of Trafalgar as a living, lasting memorial to Lord Collingwood.

As part of this year's bicentenary commemoration, there will be a special Northumbrian music concert on March 5 at Morpeth Town Hall; Collingwood related events at the April Morpeth Northumbrian Gathering; an Antiquarian Society exhibition in June and a talk by Max Adams 'Collingwood after Trafalgar' in September.

The residents of Morpeth are looking forward to being part of the Collingwood 2010 festival. It is a pleasure to be part of such a well-organised, diverse series of events.

~ Tamsin Lilley – Heritage Officer for the Greater Morpeth Development Trust

THE MAYOR OF MORPETH

COLLINGWOOD has often been referred to as 'the forgotten hero', for ever in the shadow of Lord Nelson. We in Morpeth rather like to think of this in reverse!!

The presence of Collingwood in the town can be found not only in St Robert's Presbytery and Church grounds, the former home of Admiral Collingwood, but in the many oak trees around the town and its environs, grown from the acorns he may have scattered on his walks.

Morpeth acknowledged the greatness of its hero in 2005, as part of the 200th Anniversary of the Battle of Trafalgar, and we are delighted that once again this year will see Collingwood, commemorated in a wonderful programme of events. There is something exciting, interesting and colourful for everyone, and it gives me great pleasure to welcome you in particular to those that will take place in and around Morpeth.

*~ **Ken Brown***

~ A True Sea Dog ~

ON 6 February 1804 the 14-year old Robert Hay, who had run away to sea just a year before, recorded his impression of Cuthbert Collingwood: "A better seaman, a better friend to seamen, a greater lover and more zealous defender of his country's rights and honour, never trod a quarter-deck. He and his favourite dog Bounce were well known to every member of the crew."

In sailing warships the weatherside of the quarterdeck was always reserved for the admiral or captain of the ship but Bounce, of course, knew nothing of this point of etiquette, and young Robert remembered that when the ship tacked "at any hour of the night Collingwood would be on deck, accompanied by Bounce, where they would stand on the weather gangway snuffing up the midnight, with his eye glancing through his long night glass all round the horizon." It is not clear whether Hay meant that Collingwood or Bounce was "snuffing up the air" but it's clear that Collingwood and Bounce were inseparable.

Bounce's breed is unknown: possibly a Newfie or a Menorcan rabbit hound or, some assert, a springer or an English sheepdog. Bounce, then

Bounce may have been a Spanish pointer like this one engraved by Thomas Bewick.

a puppy, and Collingwood first sailed together in the 28-gun frigate *Mermaid* in 1790. The puppy grew quickly and Collingwood wrote to his sister Mary in May that year: "My dog is a charming creature, everybody admires him but he is grown as tall as the table I am writing on."

Although a strong dog who, when he was young, delighted in swimming after his master when he went ashore in his boat, Bounce was not very brave and didn't like the noise when the guns were fired, and in battle he was tied up down on the dark orlop deck.

Bounce certainly visited Newcastle because there exists the orders for shipping him up the coast, and when Collingwood was at home in Morpeth he loved to walk the hills with his dog and with a handful of acorns in his pocket to plant along the way.

(Before the Battle of Trafalgar Collingwood wrote: "Bounce is my only pet now, and he is indeed a good fellow." If Nelson visited Collingwood in his ship, Bounce was probably under the table as the great men talked over their plans to beat the French and Spanish fleets.)

After Collingwood was made a baron he wrote to his family, "I am out of all patience with Bounce. The consequential airs he gives himself since he became a right honourable dog, are insufferable. He considers it beneath his dignity to play with commoners' dogs, and truly thinks that he does them grace when he condescends to lift up his leg against them. This, I think, is carrying the insolence of rank to the extreme, but he is a dog that does it!"

Privately Collingwood sometimes compared his officers to Bounce. In 1807 he wrote complaining about a young officer that " 'tis like teaching a rook to sing, or Bounce to play the fiddle — a long labour lost — for though Bounce is a dog of talents, I suspect he would make but a discordant fiddler." And a year later he wrote to his wife about the son of a mutual acquaintance: "He is of no more use here as an officer than Bounce is, and not near so entertaining."

Towards the end of their seagoing days together Collingwood recorded that Bounce was very well and very fat: "Yet he seems not to be content, and sighs so piteously these long evenings, that I am obliged to sing him to sleep."

Sadly, in 1809 Bounce fell overboard and drowned. Collingwood grieved greatly at his death, writing to his sister from his flagship, *Ville de Paris:* "You will be sorry to hear my poor dog Bounce is dead. I am afraid he fell overboard in the night. He is a great loss to me. I have few comforts but he was one, for he loved me. Everybody sorrows for him. He was wiser than many who hold their heads higher and was grateful to those who were kind to him."

"What shall I say of Bounce?" replied Collingwood's cousin, "I am really more sorry than I ought to be for any animal. I do indeed lament with you over him."

Clearly Bounce was everything to Collingwood that a good dog should be.

~ *Peter Hore*

Captain Hore has published a dozen books since the 1990s including 'News of Nelson'.

~ COLLINGWOOD'S CATHEDRAL ~

CUTHBERT Collingwood, Newcastle's most illustrious military hero, was born on September 29,1748, just yards from the venerable St. Nicholas's Church (now the Cathedral) at the family home in 'Head of the Side' — the position of which is marked by a bust of the admiral above a doorway to Milburn House.

The son of a none-too-successful merchant, young Collingwood was the seventh of ten children, and having three surviving elder sisters and two younger brothers, he will have grown up in a bustling, if impecunious, household on what was then the busiest thoroughfare in Newcastle.

His formative years were spent in this immediate location and living so close-by, he will have been perfectly familiar with St. Nicholas's. He was baptised here, his family will have worshiped here and in his youth he will have passed several times a day on his way to and from the Grammar School by the Westgate. Doubtless, as a boy he will have played in the churchyard and in later life, aged 42 and by then a captain, he was married in St. Nicholas's to Sarah Blackett, daughter of the Mayor of Newcastle, John Erasmus Blackett.

Collingwood's monument at the north west corner of the Cathedral was erected in 1821 two years after the death of his widow, Sarah, and at the expense of their two daughters Sarah and Mary Patience. It was originally positioned against the south west pillar of the crossing where the brass lectern now stands. The sculptor, John Charles Felix Rossi (1762-1839) was also responsible for the monuments of other military commanders of the Napoleonic Wars, mainly in St. Paul's Cathedral. Of Lady Collingwood's own memorial (a stone set in the floor) a record of the inscription exists but sadly the location is unknown.

The Collingwood monument is the focus each October 21 of the short but colourful Trafalgar Day Ceremony attended by the Lord Mayor of Newcastle, the Sheriff and members of the City Council, together with representatives of the Royal Navy, Royal Marines, Royal Naval Reserve (HMS *Calliope*), the Newcastle upon Tyne Trinity House, Newcastle Royal Grammar School, Sea Cadets and members of the Collingwood family.

This ceremony, while commemorating an illustrious son of Newcastle and a famous victory in the fight against tyranny, has of late guided our thoughts and prayers towards today's areas of conflict in which the forces of the Crown are struggling to establish peace and stability.

With these things very much in mind the Dean and Chapter of the Cathedral will welcome our guests to a special Service of Commemoration on March 7 to mark the 200th anniversary, *to the day,* of the death of Lord Collingwood. Later this year a Flower Festival will take place in the Cathedral to celebrate the work of the 'Sailors, Soldiers and Airmen's Families Association' (SSAFA). Named 'Heroes — Growing Support for those who Serve', the event builds on Collingwood

The monument to Collingwood sculpted by J. C. F. Rossi, erected in 1821.

as an example of a local hero of the past. And of course on October 21 the Trafalgar Day Ceremony will again be observed with, it is hoped, representatives from the Nelson Society as well as our usual guests.

As a people it is our duty to acknowledge the debt we owe to the members of our armed forces, both present and past, and it would be good to think that Collingwood, unassuming as he was, would be quietly pleased with our efforts.

~ Gordon Scott

NIGEL SHERLOCK, DL FRSA
LORD LIEUTENANT OF TYNE AND WEAR

AS the Lord Lieutenant of Tyne and Wear, I am very pleased that a commemoration is to take place to mark the bicentenary of Vice-Admiral Collingwood's death. The various accounts of his life and his achievements can teach us values that are still hugely relevant today and we may be rightly proud that he was born on Tyneside.

Like many, I feel I should know more about the man and look forward with anticipation to the programme of events in the Collingwood 2010 Festival, which seeks to share his legacy with the people of the North East and with visitors to the region during the year ahead.

~ CUTHBERT COLLINGWOOD'S SCHOOLDAYS ~

GIVEN that it has been in existence since the 16th century, and the important role it has played in the life of the city, the Royal Grammar School, Newcastle, has had its share of distinguished former students (known as Old Novos). Cuthbert Collingwood is one of them.

In truth, Collingwood's time at the school was probably very brief; the co-editor of the school's history, Brian Mains, believes it was probably as little as six months (unfortunately the school's records for this period were lost a long time ago). By the age of 13, Collingwood was at sea. The reason for his brief stay was in all probability the same reason for his attendance in the first place.

Though from a distinguished gentry family, the Collingwoods had no money. John Scott, who as Lord Eldon was Lord Chancellor for 20 years from 1807, recalled that Collingwood and he 'were class fellows at Newcastle. We were placed at that school because neither his father or mine could afford to place us elsewhere.'

It was a very different institution then, of course, based upon a 'pure classical foundation' overseen by the 'hard but highly capable' Head, Hugh Moises: 'Latin was the meat course and salads and desserts were few'.

The success of Collingwood and Scott shines a light on the social and educational history of the RGS. Like similar ancient grammar schools up and down the land, the RGS produced many high-powered and successful people over the centuries. Some, coming from wealthy families, will have given the impression that future success was inevitable given the silver spoon they were born with. Collingwood and Scott may have been 'gentle born', but were relatively impoverished.

The RGS of the 18th century had a pretty comprehensive social intake, varying from the sons of clergymen and gentry, to the 'middling sort', and sons of craftsmen and even 'menial servants' who won their way from truly poor homes into the school and to success beyond. It was for them, above all, that the school was founded, undoubt-edly in some form some decades before it was officially endowed and put on a more secure footing by Thomas Horsley's bequest of 1545. It was modestly priced to those who could pay fees, but was free (apparently) to the poor as well as to the sons of Freemen.

For Collingwood, and his financially challenged family, the route to success in life was the Royal Navy. University required substantial funds or, for the few, a scholarship; the army needed the purchase of a commission and private funding beyond that; the law demanded capital too. The Navy offered what amounted to free entry, an education, a career structure and the lure of prize money and glory.

Perhaps we must confess that even the exciting range of extra-curricular opportunities a school like the RGS offers cannot quite match the challenge of being at sea as a midshipman, age 13, on a fully equipped frigate! One wonders what a modern regulatory framework would have made of the dangers and ferocious discipline of such a life, however.

A school such as the RGS is proud of its distinguished Old Novos, ranging from politicians to musicians, architects to academics. To have as one of them a genuine local hero, and one of the great sailors of a nation and region with a great maritime history, is naturally a source of great pride. Collingwood left an indelible mark on European history as admiral, politician and diplomat, playing a pivotal role in saving Europe from Napoleonic domination; many more played perhaps less distinguished, but no less heroic, roles in the defence of freedom in the two world wars.

The school is delighted to be involved in the bicentennial celebrations. Collingwood may have only been with us a short time, though his affection for the area remained intact all his life. Upon news of his death the *Newcastle Courant* praised a 'highly distinguished and gallant townsman', whose 'services will forever be in the memory of a grateful country'. Those words his old school can happily echo.

~ Simon Tilbrook, Head of History, RGS

COUNCILLOR MIKE COOKSON, LORD MAYOR OF NEWCASTLE UPON TYNE

LORD Collingwood's significant role during the final stages of the Battle of Trafalgar should never be underestimated and this Festival will give us a perfect opportunity to learn why he was so important to this country and our history. As one of our city's favourite sons he was a dedicated member of the Royal Navy showing leadership and heroism and was proud to call the North East his home.

The Collingwood 2010 Festival will give everyone the chance to learn more about Collingwood, his distinguished career and his legacy. As Lord Mayor of Newcastle, I am proud to represent the city as we mark this important anniversary and look forward to meeting many of the organisations with connections to Lord Collingwood during the Festival. I would like to give them and all our visitors, including his descendants, a very warm welcome.

~ HMS COLLINGWOOD HISTORY ~

THE present HMS *Collingwood* was commissioned in early 1940 as a new-entry training camp for hostilities-only ratings. The establishment comprised four training divisions and a gunnery section responsible for the final three weeks of a class's training. Shortly after, a separate signal section was added under a Signal Commander for the training of Ordinary Signalman and Ordinary Telegraphists.

After the war, the Electrical Branch was formed to maintain, design and prove increasingly complex radars, sonars and communications systems. HMS *Collingwood* became the School of Electrical Engineering in 1946 and took over the training of all officers and ratings, with the exception of the Fleet Air Arm, in the maintenance of electrical and radio equipment in the Fleet. Subsequently the branch became responsible for weapons and became known as the Weapon Electrical Engineering Branch, later still becoming the Weapon Engineering sub-specialisation on passing responsibly for

The first HMS Collingwood, a 2,585 ton Second Rater with 80 guns, launched at Pembroke in 1841.

ties with Morpeth, where Admiral Collingwood had a home.

The present establishment is the fourth HMS *Collingwood*. The first was a 2,585-ton Second Rater with 80 guns, launched at Pembroke in 1841. She was possibly the last wooden battleship and served in the Pacific station for some time as the Flagship of Rear Admiral Sir George Seymour. On decommissioning she was eventually sold in 1867 for £8,531.

The second ship to bear the name was a 9,500-ton twin-screw barbette battleship, commissioned in Portsmouth in 1887. She served in the Mediterranean for many years before being broken up in Newcastle in 1909.

The third HMS *Collingwood* was a Dreadnought of 19,250 tons launched at Devonport in 1908. Her life seems to have been spent entirely as a unit of the First Battle Squadron under Admiral Jellicoe. During this time she won battle honours at Jutland in 1916 with Prince Albert (later King George VI) serving in her as a Midshipman. She paid off at Portsmouth in March 1922.

The Queen Mother presented the battle ensign worn at the Battle of Jutland to the present establishment.

HMS *Collingwood* is now home of the Maritime Warfare School (MWS), also encompassing the Defence Diving School, Phoenix Training Group at HMS Excellent and the Royal Navy School of Physical Training. The aim of the MWS is to train Officers and Ratings for the Fleet ready to fight and win.

~ HMS *Collingwood*

electrical generation and distribution to the Marine Engineers.

On the demise of HMS *Mercury* in 1993, history turned full circle and a Communications Faculty was added in the establishment, responsible for the operational communications training of the warfare branch ratings and officers. Further expansion followed in 1995 when the System Engineering and Management Training Group was formed to take on the application training of junior Weapon Engineer Officers following the closure of the Royal Naval Engineering College at Manadon.

HMS *Collingwood* still maintains close

The second HMS Collingwood, a 9,500 ton twin-screw barbette battleship, commissioned Portsmouth in 1887.

~ HMS CALLIOPE ~

The North East's Modern Royal Navy

HMS *Calliope* is the principal Royal Naval Reserve Unit for the North and North East of England. It is the home base for some 100 naval reservists drawn from all walks of life and all parts of the region. The Unit's role is to train and prepare part-time naval officers and ratings for duty alongside their regular service colleagues. Naval training in the unit takes place on Monday evenings, on regular weekends throughout the year and at various other locations across the country and internationally.

By virtue of sea-faring tradition and close community links to shipping, commerce and the sea, the North East has always proved to be an excellent recruiting ground for sailors and the Royal Navy in particular. This is as true today as ever. *Calliope* provides the opportunity for those who wish to serve in the Royal Navy on a part-time basis to do so and *Calliope* officers and ratings have served with distinction in two world wars. This tradition of service continues today with personnel from the unit being deployed on current live operations throughout the Middle East and elsewhere.

The Tyne Division of what was originally called the Royal Naval Volunteer Reserve (RNVR) was formed in 1905 and HMS *Calliope* was chosen as its drill ship and depot. Rather fittingly for the Collingwood 2010 Festival the officers and men (there were only men then) from Calliope paraded for the first time in public in 1905, at the Collingwood Monument, Tynemouth; probably on the occasion of the Trafalgar centenary and thus began the particularly close links between the 'local' Royal Navy and Collingwood which have endured for over 100 years. In 1951 the original *Calliope* was replaced by HMS Falmouth which was renamed *Calliope* and berthed at Elswick. In 1968, Tyne Division moved ashore to a new HQ in its current location near the Millennium Bridge between the Sage Music Centre and River Tyne.

The first HMS *Calliope* was launched in 1808, but it is the third, a Calypso class cruiser, launched in 1884, and which went on to be the first drill ship in the River Tyne, which is probably the most famous. During her operational service this ship was to gain a place in nautical history when she performed one of the late 19th century's most notable feats of seamanship, escaping from the harbour at Apia, Samoa, during the violent hurricane that struck on 15-16 March 1889, sinking every other warship

The Royal Naval Reserve Unit Headquarters at Gateshead.

in the harbour. *Calliope*'s machinery and the brilliant seamanship of her crew allowed her to work her way past reefs and gain sea room to survive, a feat that six other ships of the American and German Navy were unable to achieve and which resulted in them being wrecked with heavy loss of life. Today's officers in *Calliope* commemorate this event every year by holding a mess dinner at the unit headquarters.

Calliope's Trafalgar Dinner is also a special and unique event. Each year on or near to October 21 every Royal Navy Wardroom Officer's Mess throughout the world sits down to a dinner in commemoration of Trafalgar and to drink a toast to the Immortal Memory of Admiral Lord Nelson. This tradition is maintained in *Calliope*, but with an important addition. *Calliope*'s dinner also celebrates Admiral Collingwood whose Newcastle birthplace on 'The Side' can be seen from *Calliope*'s Wardroom Mess windows.

This Geordie sailor was the perfect counterpart to the more flamboyant Nelson and it is this rather unassuming, loyal, and above all highly professional leader of sailors, *Calliope* especially honours each year, and who in himself represents a strong, enduring but very human role model for the Unit.

Calliope has a long and proud association with Gateshead, Newcastle and the region, and enjoys the Freedom of the City of Newcastle. Her personnel are regularly seen at ceremonial events throughout the local area. As well as being a regional RNR HQ, *Calliope* provides essential support to visiting Royal Navy and other warships when they visit the North East. It is also used as a vital operations centre for the emergency services during public events based on the river in the vicinity of the Tyne and Millennium Bridges and when major conferences are held at the Sage. *Calliope* is delighted to provide this service to the wider community and as your local embodiment of the Royal Navy is honoured to be part of the Collingwood Festival 2010.

~ *E W G McNaught*
Cdr RNR
Commanding Officer, HMS CALLIOPE

For more information about HMS *CALLIOPE* and careers in the Royal Navy Reserve visit:
www.royalnavy.mod.uk/operations-and-support/royal-naval-reserve/training-centres/hms-calliope-gateshead

~ PILOT BOAT *COLLINGWOOD* ~

AT the official launch ceremony of the Port of Tyne Authority's brand new £750,000 pilot boat in August 2008, the new boat was named *Collingwood*' by Mrs Susan

The crew of the pilot boat Collingwood.

Collingwood-Cameron, a great-great-great niece of Admiral Lord Collingwood, who described her part in the launch as "a special honour".

The Port of Tyne had invited local schools as well as children of port employees to name the boat and there was a fantastic response with more than 250 entries and some really imaginative suggestions, including...

'Triton' – Millie age 6 "He is God of the water".

'The Zooming Cutter Rules' – Hannah age 10, "Because it will go fast and rule all the other boats".

'James Cramman' – Rachel age 7 "After my Great Granda, who built ships on the Tyne"

'Little Neptune' – Erin age 8 "Even if he is a little boat he is still King of the Tyne".

But Brian Reeve, the Port's Chief Technical Officer, said: "There were 12 entries for one name, Collingwood, and all the

judges felt this was a great name for our new boat."

The Port of Tyne is the principal port on the east coast and the port's pilot launches are essential in maintaining the prosperity of the river. They need to be all-weather boats capable of going to sea and boarding and landing pilots in any conditions. Reliability of the port's two pilot launches and survey/pilot boat is paramount and our maintenance engineers are all involved in the upkeep and repair.

Collingwood's revolutionary aluminium hull, the first example of its kind in the UK, was designed and built by Pembroke Dock-based Mustang Marine. The sharply angled hull gives a finer entry than conventional hulls whilst retaining the roll stability and the combined result is a fast vessel with an excellent ability to manoeuvre at sea.

The hull, deck and superstructure are fabricated throughout using marine grade aluminium alloy, the central helm position is arranged with all controls, instrumentation and navcomms ergonomically close to hand. The coxswain and boatman both enjoy suspension seats, three of which are also fitted for pilots.

Collingwood is also fitted with radar, satellite compass, GPS sensor, AIS (Automated Identification System) a digital

THERE has been a port on the River Tyne for almost 2,000 years. The earliest trades were in grain and forest products with the countries of Scandinavia and the Baltic. These areas are still important but the interests of the Port of Tyne now extend to the Far East, Australia, South East Asia, India, the Middle East, Canada and the Americas.

Today the Port of Tyne covers 600 acres spread equally on the north and south banks of the River Tyne and comprising five business areas — bulk and conventional cargo; car terminals, cruise and ferries, logistics and estates.

The Port of Tyne is one of the UK's largest trust ports and our aim is to provide a vibrant and sustainable port for stakeholders, the community and North East England.

We are delighted to have the opportunity to sponsor Collingwood 2010, commemorating the 200th anniversary of the death of Admiral Lord Collingwood. The North East is justifiably proud of its famous son, and the monument erected in his honour at Tynemouth is probably one of the most famous, and enduring, landmarks for all ships entering the Tyne.

~ **Andrew Moffat,**
Chief Executive Officer,
Port of Tyne

network echo sounder and two sailor 5022 VHF DSC radios.

Powered by Scania engines, the boat has a top speed at sea of 22 knots.

~ *Jennifer Dunn,*
Marketing &
Communications
Manager

~ Training Ship Collingwood ~

ONE thread that ran through Collingwood's career was his desire to train his men and as Disraeli once put it, if 'the secret of success was consistency to purpose' then training and more training was that purpose.

It was a good choice of the Navy then to name its training establishment in Fareham HMS *Collingwood*, but what of TS *Collingwood* in South Shields? Like the former that grew out of a piece of compulsory purchased marsh in 1939, the naming of TS *Collingwood* had a similar prosaic start. The Sea Cadets started as 315 Unit in November 1937 and simply shared a drill hall with other uniformed organisations in Collingwood Street, South Shields.

At the same time the Royal Marine Forces Volunteer Reserve (RMFVR) operated out of HMS *Satellite* down on

Cadets form a guard of honour at the Royal Institute of Naval Architects award evening at Newcastle Civic Centre.

the river next to the 'Halfpenny Ferry' on Comical Corner, Wapping Street. For some reason, maybe they didn't like the address, or was it the cold howling in off the sea, they decided to move further inland and took up new residence at Wingrove House, Newcastle. This left an excellent riverside property in the care of the local authority and when offered to the Sea Cadets, it was jumped at. It just seemed sensible to take the street name with them and TS *Collingwood* was formed. Now we have just passed our 72nd successful year proudly under the watchful gaze of the great man himself standing on the opposite bank of the Tyne.

As for Comical Corner, well legend has it that in the days of sail as ships navigated the lower reaches of the Tyne a bend in the river took the unaccustomed by surprise. Channelled by the high banks of North and South Shields a pronounced change in direction of the wind would leave sails flapping and ships pointing almost anywhere except where they wanted to go. It must have been a rare sight, especially to customers of the Queen's Head pub that originally occupied our riverside site.

How true the story is, I can't say for sure, but I do remember watching the Tall Ships leaving the Tyne in July 2005. I was standing on the quayside with staff and cadets at a blustery barbecueand was mightily impressed at the sight of the only ship leaving under full sail, the Sea Cadets' own *TS Royalist*.

As she approached we dipped our flag and they responded by cheering onboard. Just then and to the astonishment of all watching, I can only say that the Royalist jibbed, if a square-rigged Brig can do such a thing. She showed us a clean stern and headed diagonally off towards the other side of the river before composing herself and heading out towards the harbour. A good bit of seamanship I thought, but it did make me smile.

Note

The Sea Cadets is a voluntary youth organisation that seeks to help young people to be better equipped for life and connect them with their maritime heritage. For further information go to www.ms-sc.org.uk

Cadets from TS Collingwood will provide the honour guard at the Collingwood 2010 Festival Civic Reception in Newcastle upon Tyne and host an event at their Unit HQ.

~ *John Eltringham,*
Chairman South Shields Sea Cadets

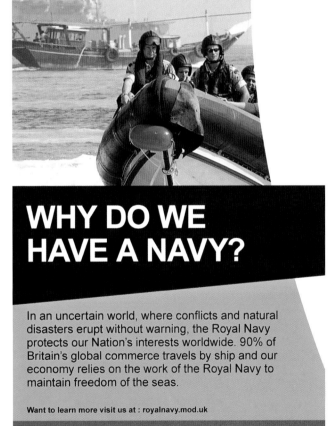

WHY DO WE HAVE A NAVY?

In an uncertain world, where conflicts and natural disasters erupt without warning, the Royal Navy protects our Nation's interests worldwide. 90% of Britain's global commerce travels by ship and our economy relies on the work of the Royal Navy to maintain freedom of the seas.

Want to learn more visit us at : royalnavy.mod.uk

~ WELCOME THE TALL SHIPS ~

HARTLEPOOL will be centre stage in August 2010 when it welcomes an impressive fleet of tall ships from around the world and up to a million visitors at the dazzling finale of the Tall Ships' Races.

The thriving North East coastal town has been chosen to host the celebrations in what will be a magnificent spectacle and what the town's Mayor Stuart Drummond has dubbed "Hartlepool's biggest party." It's also the biggest free event being held in the country this year.

The ships are due to arrive in Hartlepool on Saturday, August 7, after sailing from Kristiansand in Norway in the second and final race and they will stay until Tuesday, August 10, when they bid farewell in an impressive Parade of Sail.

The largest ships in the fleet (the 'A' Class Square Riggers) will be berthed in the town's Victoria Harbour while the smaller 'B', 'C' and 'D' Class vessels will be in Hartlepool Marina.

An enormous amount of planning is underway behind the scenes to provide hospitality and entertainment for the ships' crews and the tourists. There are also lots of opportunities for individuals and businesses to get involved in

People are helping to spread the word by using a specially-created Hartlepool Tall Ships graphic on their emails, letterheads, websites and other literature to spread the message far and wide.

Mayor Drummond said: "Hartlepool is well known for the help and the warmth of the welcome which it has extended to visiting Tall Ships over the years. We are tremendously proud to have been chosen by Tall Ships organisers Sail Training International to be a host port for the 2010 races and we are pulling out all the stops to make this *the* event of the year. Make a date in your diary for August 2010 and join us for a spectacular event which people of all ages will remember for years to come."

For further information log onto www.hartlepooltallships2010.com, contact the Hartlepool Tall Ships Office on 01429 523420 or e-mail tallships@hartlepool.gov.uk

The Aglaia, a Class B vessel from Austria, will be one of the participants in this year's Tall Ships' races.

Hartlepool Tall Ships 2010, ranging from opportunities to crew a Tall Ship to becoming an ambassador for the event by joining the Volunteer team. It is also hoped that Tall Ships visitors will support some of the events taking place in the region as part of the Collingwood 2010 Festival.

~ THE TRAFALGAR WOODS ~

STORIES of Collingwood and his pocket full of acorns abound, to the extent that it seems at times as if the Admiral was responsible for planting every oak tree that stands in Northumberland today. While some, such as those commonly known as the 'Collingwood Oaks' in College Valley near Wooler, have a clear historical connection, others elsewhere may in truth have been 'planted' in the bars of the country inns for which the area is renowned.

What is beyond discussion, however, is the result of 'The Trafalgar Woods' project – a co-operative venture between the Woodland Trust and the Society for Nautical Research, which formed part of the 'Trafalgar 200 Festival' in 2005.

New woods were planted across Britain and each named for one of the 27 ships of the line in the fleet (plus a wood for at least six of the support vessels) at the Battle of Trafalgar. In all, some 15,000 trees were planted at the 33 sites, covering 858 acres

A number of the woods are in the North East of England, being the *Royal Sovereign* wood at Throckley near Newcastle upon Tyne, the *Ajax* wood near Durham and the *Entreprenante* wood near Darlington. A little further afield yet still within easy reach is the *Revenge* wood near Scarborough.

The trees were all planted by schoolchildren and the project had a strong educational purpose, aiming both to inform and inspire. By now, the trees are around five years old and, hopefully, well established. Their future will not lie in the hulls of the Navy's 'wooden walls', as Collingwood intended when he planted his acorns, but instead as a lasting tribute and living lesson for generations of youngsters to come.

~ COLLINGWOOD PRIMARY SCHOOL ~

COLLINGWOOD School, North Shields, was opened in 1929 as Collingwood Infants School. On the closure of Chirton School through bomb damage during the war, a junior school was opened in 1955, and these were amalgamated to make a primary school during the 1970s. We think that the school (and the ward) were named after Lord Collingwood because originally he owned the land and we have a facsimile letter from him asking for rents nearby.

The school uses Lord Collingwood's motto 'Loyalty and Service', and each school year we talk about Cuthbert Collingwood as someone to look up to. The motto is not easy to explain to younger children especially, but we try to say that he was a man who put other people first, especially his duty to his country.

We worked hard to acquire more information about Collingwood during the Trafalgar celebrations and had a special ceremony with a commemorative plaque put in our refurbished school garden which was opened by local MP, Alan Campbell. Children had great fun creating large figureheads for the five ships of the line most closely associated with Collingwood. These ships then became the names for our houses in school, and children gain team points for their ships for a weekly competition.

This year we plan to do a lot more research about Collingwood and we are working with Trinity House Newcastle, Live Theatre and the Customs House in South Shields on a creative event to take place in September. Prior to that our choir will sing on the anniversary of Lord Collingwood's death at his monument in Tynemouth.

~ Dr James Crinson, Head Teacher

ON behalf of North Tyneside Council I wish to congratulate the Collingwood 2010 Festival Committee for organising an exciting programme of celebratory activities which befit the memory of Admiral Lord Collingwood.

As a council we are proud of our heritage and Collingwood's association with our Borough. The greatest statue of the Admiral stands proud at the mouth of the Tyne and symbolises the Borough's maritime and naval history. These celebrations across the region underline Collingwood's significance and achievements. The programme for 2010 provides further opportunity for local people and, in particular, our children and young people to learn about and celebrate their heritage. We are proud to play our part in the celebrations and wish every success to all our partners in ensuring that Collingwood's legacy is acknowledged for generations to come.

~ Linda Arkley,
Elected Mayor of North
Tyneside

~ "COLLINGWOOD 2010, MENORCA" ~

ONE of Menorca's foremost groups, the Asociación Menorca Britannia actively encourages and promotes a better understanding of the historic and cultural links between the Menorquin people and the British community. Since 1708 and the arrival of the British during the reign of Queen Anne, subsequently to become a British Crown Colony on the signing of the Treaty of Utrecht in 1713, there has been a unique and deep-rooted British influence (and mutual friendship) which can be clearly seen

ASOCIACIÓN MENORCA BRITANNIA

by today's visitors. Although Great Britain voluntarily handed Menorca back to the Spanish crown at the Treaty of Amiens in 1802 that friendship continues to the present day.

Cuthbert Collingwood's outstanding career is known to most with an interest in naval history and is only overshadowed, perhaps mistakenly, by that of his great friend Admiral Lord Nelson. It was after the unfortunate and premature death of Nelson during the Battle of Trafalgar that this great man's true courage, humanity and dedication to his country were shown and when his connection with Spain and in particular Menorca began.

Bravely leading the battle from the front until its final conclusion, Collingwood showed his great humanity during the storm that followed by sending out boats to rescue hundreds of Spanish and French seamen from stricken or sinking ships. He arranged the safe landing of these "prisoners" in Cadiz and into the hands of the Governor of Andalucia, the Condé de Solana. A friendship was cemented with the gift of barrels of wine being sent to the British ships. Reportedly in return, a return gift of a keg of British beer and some Cheddar cheese was given by Collingwood. Many letters between the two men display their mutual respect and friendship thereafter.

Following the Battle of Trafalgar Collingwood was sent to Port Mahón in Menorca to take charge of the British Mediterranean Fleet. During the last five years of his life Collingwood dutifully carried out his orders to blockade the French south coast ports, patrol the Gulf of Leon and assist the Spanish in defending their mainland coastline and the Balearic Islands.

As his shore base, Collingwood took residence in a splendid colonial style house "Fonduco" overlooking the harbour above where his flagship was anchored. This is now a charming privately-run hotel retaining all the features and alterations carried out during his time here

It was in the year prior to his death and during the Napoleonic War that Collingwood ordered an escort of frigates to a merchant ship bringing to Menorca one of the world's largest organs ever manufactured. This was installed in the parish church of Sta. Maria in Mahón. With more than 3,000 pipes and four keyboards the organ is played every day and is just part of the heritage left by Lord Collingwood on Menorca. This world famous organ is also celebrating it's 200th anniversary this year.

During his last year Collingwood was ailing and in pain spending many periods bedridden but he stoically "soldiered on" until, very ill and dying he was carried to his ship to make his way to England. Unfortunately he died on board still within Menorcan waters.

The Asociación Menorca Britannia is proud to be arranging the 200th anniversary commemoration in Menorca of the life of Lord Collingwood, completing the full circle, so to speak, from his place of birth to his last honourable post and eventual place of death.

The Asociación is also honoured to present a specially commissioned sculptured life size bronze bust of Admiral Lord Collingwood which is to be placed in a prominent position near the harbour to leave a lasting memorial which all the residents and visitors to Menorca can admire in the years ahead.

With the commemorative event in Newcastle during the weekend of March 6-7, it is appropriate that we are holding the event in Menorca at the end of that month. This gives ample opportunity for all who wish to attend both.

The sculptor's model for the new life-size bronze bust.

In co-operation with the Island Government, Mahón Town Council and various sponsors, the programme is expected to be as follows:

March 27 — Arrival of the Royal Navy; Civic reception by Consell Insular (Island Government); Organ, choir and piano recital in Sta. Maria Church. March 28 — Unveiling and dedication of the sculpture of Admiral Collingwood with the ship's company in attendance

~ Bryce Lyons

For further information and enquiries contact, email: menorcabritannia@msn.com or visit www.menorca.es or www.menorcabritannia.org

~ COLLINGWOOD NEW ZEALAND ~

LOCATED at the north-west corner of the South island of New Zealand, in the Golden Bay area of the Tasman Region, Collingwood was originally a small Maori settlement named Aorere, to which the English name of Gibbstown was given. The gold boom of the mid 19th century led to a rapid rise in population and in 1857 the provincial government had plans drawn up for a new town, to which the name of Collingwood was assigned in honour of Admiral Lord Collingwood.

The town was even proposed as the capital of New Zealand at one stage but, in the event, the boom was short lived and this never happened. Fire destroyed the settlement in 1859, another fire in 1904 destroyed the rebuilt village and as recently as 1967 fire struck again, burning down the hall, hotel and two shops.

Today's Collingwood is a mixture of old and new. Reminders of the past are found in St. Cuthbert's Church (1873), the courthouse (1901) and post office buildings. The crumbling grave-markers in the Old Collingwood cemetery bear testimony to a difficult past involving the fires, floods, epidemics, shipwrecks and other trials of early colonial life.

In 2005, to mark the 200th anniversary of the Battle of Trafalgar, a series of commemorative and community events were organised in Collingwood, and indeed in Nelson, some 77 miles to the south, and it is hoped to mark 2010 in similar style.

Richard Kempthorne, the Mayor of Tasman District, said: "I send best wishes to everyone involved in commemorating the 200th anniversary of the death of Admiral Lord Collingwood and the festival which will recognise his life and accomplishments.

We are proud to have our town Collingwood named after him. I believe this to be the Collingwood which is the greatest distance from his original birthplace and this beautiful, rather isolated but environmentally and culturally dramatic area seems to me to be very appropriately named in honouring a great achiever in the Royal Navy.

I join the rest of our community in hoping that you have a remarkable time commemorating this anniversary."

Mayor
Richard Kempthorne

~ COLLINGWOOD CANADA ~

ALTHOUGH an ocean away, Admiral Cuthbert Collingwood has had a profound impact on the small, bustling settlement that proudly bears his name in Ontario. In 1834, a township to the west of Hen and Chickens Harbour was officially renamed Collingwood Township. Later, in 1853, the Town of Collingwood was christened by a group of railway officials who were charting a rail line to connect the harbour with the City of Toronto.

Collingwood's harbour was a hive of shipbuilding activity and the closure of the shipyard in 1986 had a drastic effect on the community. Collingwood now relies on its idyllic location on Georgian Bay and its close proximity to Blue Mountain, one of Ontario's largest ski resorts, as a tourist destination.

The pride that Collingwood's citizens hold for our namesake remains strikingly clear given the number of buildings that boast the Admiral's name. Additionally, a Collingwood resident commissioned a large oil painting of Admiral Collingwood by a local artist to decorate the council chambers in Town Hall. This impressive painting was officially unveiled in the presence of two of Admiral Collingwood's descendents.

In recognition of Trafalgar 2005, the Town of Collingwood installed an exhibition in Town Hall for public viewing. The exhibit was then transferred to The Collingwood Museum where it remained for three years. Similarly, a memorial exhibit will be installed in The Collingwood Museum to honour the Admiral's bi-centennial.

The inherent link between Collingwood's role as an important shipping port and Admiral Collingwood's seafaring history will continue to highlight the Town of Collingwood's formative years in periods of transformation.

~ Melissa Shaw, The Collingwood Museum

"ON behalf of members of the town council and the people of Collingwood, may I commend the Collingwood 2010 Festival Committee for organising this event and wish you well in your celebration of the life of Vice-Admiral Collingwood.

Events here in 2005 brought about an increased awareness of the history surrounding the Battle of Trafalgar and we look to this year to develop that into a greater understanding of one of the principal combatants, the man after whom our town is named.

We look forward to learning more of what is happening in England, in Collingwood, New Zealand, and in Menorca, Spain, as the year progresses. We are proud of our heritage and feel privileged to be part of a celebration which is bringing communities together across this planet in the name of Collingwood."

~ Christopher J. Carrier,
Mayor of Collingwood,
Ontario

~ ALE COMMEMORATES THE ADMIRAL ~

A SPECIAL Admiral Lord Collingwood Ale has been produced by the award-winning Wylam Brewery for the Collingwood 2010 Festival.

Described as a "thirst-quenching pale ale", the brew is now available in bottles and on draught at real ale pubs including The Tyne, the Brewery's 'tap' which stands on the riverside at the mouth of the Ouseburn, only a 15-minute walk from the Newcastle street where Collingwood was born.

John Boyle, managing director of the Tyne Valley-based brewery

Captain Healy and Matt Boyle of Wylam Brewery drink to the Admiral.

said: "We are delighted to be associated with the Festival and proud to support it with a new brew to celebrate the life of one of our most famous Newcastle sons. Demand was so strong that we sold most of the first 3,200 litre batch in a couple of days."

"Captain Stephen Healy, chairman of the Collingwood 2010 Festival Committee, said: "We're delighted to have Wylam Brewery on board. They have produced a superb beer to help us celebrate the life and achievements of one of our greatest heroes."

THE Society for Nautical Research is pleased to be able to support the Collingwood 2010 Festival through its sponsorship of this commemorative brochure, which it is hoped will form a permanent memoir of this season of celebrations to mark the bicentenary of Vice-Admiral Lord Collingwood.

The Society for Nautical Research publishes *The Mariner's Mirror,* the world's pre-eminent English-language nautical journal. In its pages you can read about research from members and non-members alike into all kinds of matters such as seafaring, ships and shipbuilding throughout the ages, the language and customs of the sea, and, in fact, any topic of nautical interest.

THE SOCIETY FOR NAUTICAL RESEARCH

The Society also supports and encourages research into maritime history and nautical archaeology. It sponsors conferences, lectures and seminars on maritime historical subjects, buys paintings and other works of art for the National Maritime Museum at Greenwich, and funds heritage projects such as the preservation of Nelson's flagship, HMS *Victory* — with which Cuthbert Collingwood would have been so familiar.

The Society was founded in 1910 and so is celebrating its centenary in 2010. To join or for more information please go to our website http://www.snr.org.uk. Or write to The Lodge, The Drive, Hellingly, Hailsham, East Sussex, BN27 4EP.

~ Professor Richard Harding, Chairman

~ TRINITY HOUSE, NEWCASTLE ~

AS Master of Trinity House, Newcastle upon Tyne, I am proud to be associated with the various organised functions which will mark the 200th anniversary of the death of Admiral Lord Cuthbert Collingwood, throughout 2010.

After the Battle of Trafalgar in 1805 Collingwood was honoured by being offered the Honorary Freedom of the House by the Master and Brethren. This was subsequently accepted by Collingwood in a letter (which the House still holds) as the Admiral never returned to his home shores after Trafalgar. This incidentally makes Collingwood the only Honorary Member ever created in *absentia.*

In about 1825 it was originally planned to erect a Collingwood monument in the Courtyard of Trinity House on the Newcastle Quayside, but this was eventually sited

at Tynemouth, overlooking the entrance to the River Tyne.

Work is now underway to develop a memorial to Admiral Collingwood on land adjacent to Trinity House. This will take the form of a public art structure depicting a 20-foot (6m) high 'ocean wave' and it is hoped that with sufficient funding this will be in place during the summer of 2010.

Trinity House Brethren have for over 500 years looked after the safety of seafarers on these coasts and support all efforts to promote the traditional maritime heritage of this region.

The Collingwood celebrations are another chapter in our long history and we trust that all those involved will receive the full support which the occasion deserves.

~ Captain Rudyard C. Shipley

~ COLLINGWOOD 2010 FESTIVAL PROGRAMME ~

23rd January: Official Opening of the Festival.

23rd January-27th June: Discovery Museum, Newcastle upon Tyne. Exhibition: 'Collingwood – A Northumbrian Abroad'. Free admission. For more information, see www.twmuseums.org.uk/discovery or tel: 0191-2326789.

5th-7th March: Visit of the 1805 Club to the region: series of private and public events. For more information, see www.1805club.org

5th March: Morpeth Town Hall, Market Place, Morpeth. In association with the Morpeth Gathering: 7.30pm: Celebration Concert: Alistair Anderson, Ernie Gordon and Friends, the Border Directors, MC Alex Swailes.Tickets £8, £6.50 concessions. Contact Kim Bibby-Wilson, tel: 01670-513308.

6th March: Morpeth Town Hall. Storytelling by Sedayne: 10am and 1pm: Free: 'Stories of the Sea'.

6th March: Morpeth Town Hall. Film showing of 'Master and Commander' 2pm: Free admission, seating as available. (Rated PG-13).

6th March: Newcastle upon Tyne Civic Centre. 7.30pm: Lord Mayor's Civic Dinner, to honour Admiral Lord Collingwood, by invitation only.

7th March: Newcastle City Centre. Naval Parade: 11.45am: Civic Centre to Castle Garth (Moot Hall), via the Cathedral Church of St. Nicholas. HM Royal Marines Band (Plymouth), detachments from HMS Collingwood, HMS Cumberland, HMS Calliope, RMR Tyne, RGS CCF and SCC (Tyne & Wear).

7th March: Cathedral Church of St. Nicholas, Newcastle upon Tyne. 12.30pm: Service of Commemoration organised by the 1805 Club with the assistance of the Dean of Newcastle and Newcastle City Council. Public welcome, but limited seating available.

7th March: Collingwood Monument, Tynemouth. 3.00pm: Commemorative Event organised by North Tyneside Council. Service, gun and warship salutes. For more information, see www.northtyneside.gov.uk and search 'events' or tel: 0845-2000101.

7th March: The 'Collingwood Arms', Brandling Village, Jesmond, Newcastle upon Tyne. An evening of Trafalgar and music, with house band 'Strings Attached'. 7.30 10.30pm. Free admission. For more information, tel: Jamie Hansell on 0191-2095388.

10th March: Bewick Hall, Newcastle City Library. 6-7pm: 'Lord Collingwood 200 years on' – a talk by Max Adams. Free admission, but seat booking required. Contact information@newcastle.gov.uk; tel: 0191-2774100.

18th March: HMS *Calliope,* South Shore Road, Gateshead. In association with the Nautical Institute (North East Branch): 6.30pm 'Trafalgar, the weather and Collingwood': an illustrated talk by Dr. Dennis Wheeler: free admission, but booking required: contact David Byrne: dbyrne@nodent.co.uk tel: 0191-2173660.

22nd March: The 'Lit and Phil', Westgate Road, Newcastle upon Tyne. In association with Tyne Bridge Publishing. 6 pm: 'Collingwood and Nelson: a Unique Friendship', an illustrated talk by Max Adams. Tickets £2, book in advance only at the 'Lit and Phil', or tel: 0191-2320192.

27th-30th March: Port Mahon, Menorca, Spain. Commemorative Event: Civic Reception, organ recital, unveiling of statue of Collingwood, RN warship visit, displays, visits, tours, for details see www.meorcanbritannia.org or contact menorcabritannia@msn.com

1st-2nd May: Newcastle Arts Centre and the Newcastle upon Tyne Trinity House. North East Centre for Lifelong Learning 2-day workshop: 'The Life and Times of Admiral Collingwood'. With Max Adams, Dr. Tony Barrow, John Sadler. Cost: £55 (£35 for NECLL members). For details contact the Centre for Lifelong Learning, tel: 0191-5152800 or www.explore.sunderland.ac.uk

12th-13th June: Morpeth Town Hall. Morpeth Antiquarian Society exhibition: joint-theme 'Lord Collingwood': Open all day: free.

14th-15th June: The Newcastle upon Tyne Trinity House, Broad Chare, Quayside, Newcastle upon Tyne. In association with the Eat! NewcastleGateshead Festival and Boldon Farmhouse Pantry: a special historical dining experience 'An evening with Collingwood',

hosted by the Deputy Master of Trinity House Newcastle; Max Adams/Tony Barrow and TV presenter John Grundy. Trafalgar themed menu designed by William Brewis, wines inclusive £45 per head. Strictly limited to 24 covers. Advance bookings. Contact: 0191-2816025.

3rd July: Royal Grammar School, Jesmond, Newcastle upon Tyne. 'RGS Day – incorporating the Collingwood legacy': Open Day, with drama, displays, etc. related to Collingwood, including the inaugural 'Collingwood Lecture', this year given by Max Adams. All welcome, free admission.

10th July: Sunderland Aged Seamen's Homes, Trafalgar Square, Hendon. Unveiling of a memorial to the Sunderland seamen who fought at the Battle of Trafalgar. Public welcome (further information-www.collingwood2010.org.uk).

13th-18th July: Cathedral Church of St. Nicholas, Newcastle upon Tyne and Sage Gateshead. Association with the SSAFA 'Heroes, Past and Present' Festival: flower and music festival. For details, see www.heroesflowerfestival.org.uk

7th-10th August: Hartlepool Quays, Hartlepool. Association with the Tall Ships 2010: see www.tallshipshartlepool2010.co.uk

9th September: Morpeth Town Hall. 7.30pm: Talk by Max Adams as part of Morpeth Heritage Open Days event, free admission (details to be confirmed).

9th October: The Sage Gateshead. 'That Noble Fellow Collingwood' – concert featuring the New Scorpion Band. For bookings and more details, see www.thesagegateshead.org or tel: 0191-4434661.

October (date to be confirmed): Sunderland. In association with the Friends of Old Sunderland Parish Church, a talk by Dr Tony Barrow 'County Durham Men at Trafalgar'.

21st October: Cathedral Church of St. Nicholas, Newcastle upon Tyne. 10.00am: Trafalgar Day Service.

23rd-24th October: Visit of the Nelson Society to the region, including AGM. Series of private and public events. For more information, see www.nelson-society.com

24th October: Close of Festival.

Other events: Unveiling of new sculpture to Collingwood near the Quayside, Newcastle upon Tyne (independent project coordinated by the Newcastle upon Tyne Trinity House and the Arts Council).

International Links: Civic and cultural contact has been established with both Collingwood, New Zealand and Collingwood, Ontario, as well as Menorca, Spain.

Education Initiative: The Collingwood 2010 Festival has established an education programme to bring Collingwood into local schools and youth groups through prepared lesson plans, drama and out-of-school visits.

For more information, see www.collingwood2010.co.uk

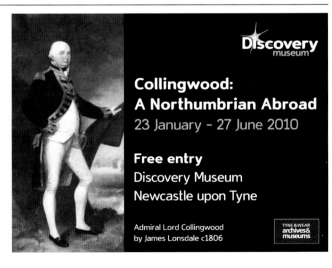

Promoting resilience in f children and young people

Lisa Bostock

Social Care Institute for Excellence

Better knowledge for better practice

First published in Great Britain in September 2004 by the Social Care Institute for Excellence (SCIE)

Social Care Institute for Excellence
1st Floor
Goldings House
2 Hay's Lane
London SE1 2HB
UK
www.scie.org.uk

Reprinted 2005

Dr Lisa Bostock is a Senior Research Analyst at the Social Care Institute for Excellence (SCIE)

Produced by The Policy Press
University of Bristol
Fourth Floor, Beacon House
Queen's Road
Bristol BS8 1QU
UK
www.policypress.org.uk

Printed and bound in Great Britain by Hobbs the Printers Ltd, Southampton.

Contents

Acknowledgements

The Social Care Institute for Excellence (SCIE) would like to thank all of the organisations and individuals who have shaped the development of this resource guide. We gratefully acknowledge the contributions from:

- the *SCIE Advisory Group on Fostering*, which is a mix of professionals, young people and policy makers set up to advise SCIE on its work around fostering and who have played an integral role in the development of this resource guide
- *A National Voice*, a user group of young people who are, or who have been, looked after in England, for embodying what this guide is about – the strengths of children and their families
- *Voices from Care Cymru*, a user group of young people who are, or who have been, looked after in Wales, who have worked with us to run creative workshops on fostering practice
- Professor *Jane Tunstill*, Royal Holloway, University of London, who provided invaluable comments on why the resource guide will be useful to practitioners and to those in service delivery development
- Professor *Robbie Gilligan*, Trinity College Dublin, whose message of hope that the lives of children in public care can be made better by promoting children's strengths, has inspired and shaped this resource guide

The author would also like to thank colleagues at SCIE for their helpful comments on drafts of this guide.

Key messages/key readings

Research findings

Practice examples

Quotes from young people, foster carers or practitioners

Poem by a young person in foster care

'What I live for'

I live for something rare and true
I'm looking for the words so that I can tell you
It contains love and happiness
The things that we really miss

Some hearts are made out of gold
But others are like stone so hard and cold
Behind their closed doors
They're screaming out but nobody knows

The feelings of anger they lock up inside
It's so hard to push these feelings aside
When you go to sleep at night
You see the birds in circled flight

And when you awaken the following day
You feel lost like the needle dropped in the hay
I live something rare and true
I've found the words to give to you

(Young person, 16 years old, from a consultation conducted by Voices from Care Cymru, a
user group of young people who are, or who have been, looked after in Wales[5])

Why childcare professionals matter

This resource guide looks at how childcare professionals can make a difference to young people's experiences of foster care.

Professionals play an important role by supporting caring relationships, ensuring that school is a positive experience, and promoting the self-esteem of children and young people in the foster care system.

This resource guide unpacks the concept of resilience and provides helpful hints for practice as well as access to further resources.

It is aimed at the qualifying and newly qualified childcare professional and outlines why they matter in the life of a foster child.

Positive relationships, at any age in the life span, can help improve poor self-image. People who take an interest, who listen, who care and love people, make others feel better. They bolster self-esteem.

> **"It's just so rewarding, so rewarding ... it's a job that's really satisfying." (foster carer[1])**

Children who are not loved at home may still develop feelings of self-worth if a relative takes an interest, a teacher appears concerned and caring, or if a social worker responds with kindness and consistency.

How childcare professionals can make a difference

Research shows that focusing on the strengths of young people is crucial to future outcomes. This means focusing on 'resilience factors', or things that help children and young people cope with adversity.

The sorts of things that buffer children and young people from unfavourable circumstances include access to a caring relationship with an adult such as a foster carer. This may also mean children having contact with their birth families and every effort should be made to get this right.

> **"Care has brought me to realise I am a person in my own right, but I know I have been very lucky – [I have a] good social worker, good residential worker and good foster parent." (16-year-old girl[2])**

The experience that foster children and young people have at school also helps them to overcome difficulties and every effort should be made to ensure that this experience is positive, by encouraging them to take part in school activities they enjoy, to help build their self-esteem.

> **"My foster carer helped me a lot ... she [has] made me more confident in my school work." (11-year-old girl[3])**

A sense of direction is very important to young people in troubled circumstances because it can provide stability and control. This means working with young people on their goals and how to reach them and helping them to build a picture of what the future may hold.

A second way of helping young people feel more in control is involving them in forums that promote the participation of young people in the development of services for looked-after children.

Practice example
Cambridge has a 'Just us' group of looked-after children who meet monthly across three localities in the county. The young people in this group were consulted during the Best Value review of the authority and also contribute ideas on how to train staff to work sensitively with looked-after children[4].

Fostering success

Fostering success is about recognising and supporting the strengths of children and their families. It is about making sure that that fostered children and young people have access to positive relationships and feel happy at school and it is about working with them to choose outcomes that reflect their own aspirations and making every effort to enable them to achieve these aspirations.

Who this resource guide is for

This resource guide is aimed primarily at qualifying and newly qualified childcare professionals and outlines why, as a professional, you matter in the life of a foster child.

This guide will be useful to the following groups:

- qualifying social workers
- post-qualifying social workers
- foster carers
- Children and Family Court Advisory and Support Service (CAFCASS) workers
- qualifying teachers
- educational psychologists

The guide also provides resources on the development of service delivery, and will interest:

- inspectors for the Commission for Social Care Inspectorate (CSCI) and the Care Standards Inspectorate for Wales (CISW)
- childcare coordinators and quality assurance managers
- members of Local Safeguarding Children Boards (LSCBs)

The resource guide will benefit your practice by:

- helping you to engage in the debate about what policies will best serve children and their families in your own agencies
- providing a review of the knowledge base on adopting a resilience-based approach and will help you in your own cases
- showing you how social work and social care agencies work, highlighting practical examples of where agencies support the strengths of children and their families

What this resource guide is about

> "It's, like, foster care ... it works differently for different people. It goes well for some people, it doesn't for others." (young person in foster care[6])

This resource guide looks at the things that children and young people live for – love, happiness and hope for the future – the kinds of things that children in foster care can really miss. It is about the strengths of children and their families and the ways in which professionals can make a difference by recognising, initiating and sustaining caring relationships, ensuring that school is a positive experience and promoting the self-esteem of children and young people in foster care.

The guide focuses on what makes foster care work well for children and young people. It looks at what is known about helping children to cope in difficult circumstances. In general, this appears to reflect what is included in the literature on resilience[8].

It unpacks the concept of resilience and provides helpful hints for practice as well as access to further resources. These messages also apply to children and young people living in residential care.

Key message
Resilience-enhancing factors include:

- building a sense of self-esteem and self-efficacy
- having at least one close tie with a committed adult
- being happy and involved at school

Foster care should be able to offer children these opportunities[11,12].

This resource guide will examine each of the resilience-enhancing factors identified above, providing practical examples of how you can promote resilience-enhancing factors for children and young people.

The guide only covers the resilience-enhancing factors highlighted in SCIE Knowledge review 5: *Fostering success: An exploration of the research literature in foster care*[8], as these are seen as crucial to future fostering outcomes. Further reading about encouraging resilience can be found in Appendix 2.

First, however, the guide will examine what is meant by child-focused fostering, and why pursuing resilience-promoting strategies is an integral part of a child-focused fostering service.

How this resource guide was created

This resource guide draws primarily, but not exclusively, on two pieces of work commissioned by SCIE that contributed to our knowledge about innovative fostering practice: Knowledge review 4: *Innovative, tried and tested: A review of good practice in fostering*[7] and Knowledge review 5: *Fostering success: An exploration of the research literature in foster care*[8].

The SCIE Advisory Group on Fostering has also provided a crucial source of knowledge on the features of a child and family-focused fostering service (see Appendix 1 for a list of participants). Contributions from children and young people who use fostering services have shaped this work.

SCIE is undertaking a range of work that relates to this guide, including practice guides on children and young people's participation in the improvement of social care services, human growth and development and good fostering practice, as well as a knowledge review on adoption research[9].

SCIE has also published Position paper 3: *Has service user participation made a difference to social care services?*[10] that looks at the impact of children and young people's participation on change and improvement in social care services.

What is child-focused fostering?

Child-focused fostering means that all decisions must be taken in the best interests of the child and that decisions should be taken in partnership with children and their families or advocates. It is the first principle of Choice Protects, a Department for Education and Skills (DfES) initiative that reviews fostering and placement services in England (www.dfes.gov.uk/choiceprotects)[13] and the National Assembly for Wales' (NAW) Children First initiative that focuses on investing in children's services in order to enable children to lead fuller, more successful lives as adults (www.childrenfirst.wales.gov.uk)[14].

In both England and Wales, the practice guidance for the *Framework for the assessment of children in need and their families* should assist professionals in making child-focused decisions about young people[15].

In this resource guide we use the term 'child-focused'. However, we recognise that this term has been criticised for its 'paternalistic' overtones, because to some it suggests that adults must adopt a focus on the child, rather than acknowledging the legal rights of children and young people to actively participate in decisions that affect their lives. The Blueprint Project for a Child-Centred Public Care System, based at the Voice for the Child in Care and supported by the National Children's Bureau, explicitly uses 'child-centred' rather than 'child-focused' in order to reinforce the importance of involving children and young people in care in decisions both at individual and service delivery level. For more information about the Blueprint Project visit www.vcc-uk.org

Children are popularly represented as passive, dependent, vulnerable and in need of protection or, alternatively, as anti-social, deviant, irresponsible and in need of firm social control. In other words, adults cast children in the role of either victim or villain[16-18]. What adults tend to think less about is how children and young people negotiate difficult circumstances and how they draw on their reserves of resilience to overcome life's adversities[19-22].

A resilience-based approach shifts attention away from focusing on problems towards a focus on the developmental strengths of children and young people. We are all born resilient but find it easier to withstand adversity in the context of caring, consoling and enduring relationships. There are a number of features that are important to resilience, particularly feeling happy and supported at school, developing self-esteem and, as we grow up, self-efficacy or the feeling of having a sense of control over our lives. The fundamental building block of resilience is an attachment to a secure base. For children in the care system, a child-focused foster system will make every effort to nurture the development of secure relationships and identify a child's social support networks[11, 23-8].

About resilience

5.1. What is resilience?

Resilience refers to the qualities that cushion a vulnerable child from the worst effects of adversity and that may help a "child or young person to cope, survive and even thrive in the face of great hurt and disadvantage"[12]. While it may not always be possible to protect a child from further adversity, finding ways to boost a child's resilience should enhance the likelihood of better long-term outcomes (see Appendix 2 for key reading on resilience).

Research evidence from follow-up studies of people who have been fostered suggests that some of the difficulties that young people initially experience upon leaving the care system – loneliness, unemployment, debt and settling down – subsequently improve, with some young people re-establishing friendly contact with foster families even after serious breakdowns. It is probably only a minority, albeit a substantial one at around 30%, who get into serious difficulties in the long term[8].

5.2. Understanding the importance of resilience

This resource guide looks at the importance of focusing on the resilience-enhancing factors in the lives of fostered children and young people. It draws on the findings of SCIE Knowledge review 5: *Fostering success: An exploration of the research literature in foster care*, which looked at the impact of fostering on outcomes for children and young people[8]. This review found that focusing on the strengths of young people is crucial to future outcomes. This means focusing on 'resilience factors', or things that help children and young people withstand adversity.

5.3. Understanding resilience-enhancing factors

Resilience-enhancing factors are the sorts of things in a child's or young person's life that help them to cope in unfavourable circumstances or times of difficulty. Resilience factors can include access to a caring relationship with adults such as foster carers and can also include contact between a child and their birth families.

The experience that foster children and young people have at school may also help them to overcome difficulties and every effort should be made to ensure that their experiences are positive, including encouraging them to take part in school activities that they enjoy to help build their self-esteem.

A sense of direction is also very important to young people in troubled circumstances because it can provide stability and control. This involves working with young people to build up a picture of what the future may hold: to develop goals and plans for reaching them[8].

5.4. Promoting self-esteem

Self-esteem is one of the fundamental building blocks of resilience. Principally, self-esteem flows from positive attachment experiences, but can be enhanced by participation in valued activities[29,30]. It is about feeling successful, not simply academically, but also in other areas such as in relationships or in spare time activities. This means that encouraging foster children to take part in school activities which they enjoy can be an important source of self-esteem[1].

> **Research finding**
> Positive relationships, at any age in the life span, can help improve poor self-concept. People who take an interest, who listen, who care and love us, make us feel better. They improve our image and bolster our self-esteem. Children who are not loved at home may nevertheless develop feelings of self-worth if a relative takes an interest, a teacher appears concerned and caring, or a residential worker responds with kindness and consistency[11].

In one study of the relationship between experiences of local authority care and offending behaviour, interviews with care leavers revealed that it was possible for young people to develop secure attachments to their foster carers, even when they were placed at a relatively late age. Furthermore, such attachments were shown to be strongly protective against offending behaviour[8].

Making the effort to show that you care about the children and young people who you work with, even if the relationship is short term, shows them that you value them. Simple displays of sincerity will increase self-esteem.

> "I always try and remember [the] birthdays of the young people that I am working with. I mean, not all of them, not if they are too young to know, but where they have low self-esteem, I try and remember their birthday, it shows them that I value them." (social worker, initial assessment team [31])

Young people confirm the importance of promoting self-esteem. A National Voice, which is an organisation run by and for young people who are or who have been in care in England, have been running a National Foster Care Campaign that aims to use the views of young people to improve fostering services. As part of the campaign, 150 young people in care took part in the *Amplify* consultation event (for more information visit www.anationalvoice.org). The *Amplify*[32] report makes the following recommendations about how to bolster the self-esteem of young people experiencing care:

- social work education should actively promote a positive image of young people from care
- local social services departments should recognise, respect and reward the unique and special skills and talents of all the young people from care in England
- young people should have access to other groups of young people from care and a 24-hour care helpline service should be established[32]

Practice examples
The Well-being, Creativity and Play project, hosted by the National Children's Bureau and funded by the Children and Young People's Unit at the DfES, aims to build self-esteem by exhibiting the art, on display at the National Gallery, of children who live in public care. For more information visit www.ncb.org.uk and www.cypu.gov.uk

Kids Company, who work with troubled children, also use art to improve self-esteem and the public image of children who are experiencing difficulties. The art installation *Shrinking childhoods* at the Tate Modern aims to create a council estate environment. In each flat, children who use Kids Company create rooms which reflect their experiences of childhood. For more information visit www.kidsco.org.uk

5.5. Promoting self-efficacy

Self-esteem is closely linked with developing a sense of self-efficacy or self-direction. Self-efficacy grows from experience. It is about qualities of optimism, persistence and believing that one's own efforts can make a difference. A person's sense of self-efficacy is improved by opportunities to take responsibility or contribute to decisions which affect the minutiae or broader trend of one's life[33,34].

Two important ways that child welfare professionals, such as managers, social workers and foster carers, can help young people in care develop a sense of self-efficacy are through:

- encouraging young people to define their own outcomes
- involving children and young people in the development of services

5.5.1. Helping young people define their own outcomes

A sense of direction is very important to young people in troubled circumstances because it provides a sense of stability and control[35]. The involvement of children and young people in planning their care is a crucial way of promoting that sense of control or self-direction. Working with young people to develop goals or outcomes can help promote a sense of what the future might hold and how to reach it[36].

Practice example
Information communications technology can have a major impact on building self-efficacy. The Royal Borough of Kingston upon Thames has developed a website to enable foster children to contribute to their local authority looked-after children review forms and to e-mail their social workers[4] (www.kingston.gov.uk).

There are a number of ways you can support young people's self-efficacy:

- involve children in discussions about their needs and their future
- help them to contribute to care plans and reviews, ensure that their wishes are always considered and where possible addressed
- give clear information, making sure that young people know about:
  - their reasons for entering into and remaining in care
  - their rights while they are in care
  - future plans and how they can influence these
- try to regard young people as resources (rather than problems) in process of seeking solutions in their lives
- encourage young people to make choices, declare preferences and define outcomes for themselves and respect these preferences[12]

Research suggests that these various opportunities and experiences can teach young people that their opinions are valuable and help them to learn how to influence, negotiate and problem solve.

5.5.2. Involving young people in service development

A second way of promoting self-efficacy is through the participation of young people in the development of services for looked-after children. Official guidance has emphasised the importance of ensuring that the voices of children in the care system are listened to and promoted.

Involving children and young people in planning and developing fostering services is a key objective of Choice Protects[13]. As part of this work the Choice Protects team asked the Fostering Network and The Who Cares? Trust to find out about children's views on commissioning. They surveyed a number of local authorities to establish how developed their children's participation services were and what children thought about the services they received. The report *Listen then commission*[37] makes a number of recommendations about how children's views can be incorporated into the commissioning process and these recommendations will be brought to the attention of local authorities. For more information visit www.thefostering.net and www.thewhocarestrust.org.uk

There are now a host of systems across local authorities for encouraging feedback from young people, including questionnaires, e-mail, meetings with senior managers and local councillors, as well as involvement in Best Value reviews[4].

Practice example

Cambridge has a 'Just us' group of looked-after children who meet monthly across three localities in the county. The young people in this group were consulted during the Best Value review of the authority and also contributed to ideas on how to train staff to work sensitively with looked-after children[4].

Some local authorities have harnessed the potential of information communications technology to promote children's participation and improve their service to young people.

Practice example

The Kids in Care Together group, set up by Norfolk County Council has established a website (www.kict.norfolk.gov.uk/kict) with helpful information for looked-after children, including foster children and young people. The group provides advice to the social services department and has had a direct impact on policy and practice evaluation and change[4].

The Tunnel Light Project set up by Lincolnshire Social Services uses web-based technologies to strengthen the relationships between its family placement service, foster carers, adoptive parents, looked-after children and young people and the public. The creation of their website www.family-lincs.org.uk has been the centrepiece of this project. The project has four main aims:

- to create appropriate e-support between families and the Lincolnshire family placement service

- to establish e-communities between foster families and looked after children
- to provide alternatives to traditional education and training programs, the development of management policies as part of the local authority's e-government agenda and to provide the general public with information about fostering and adoption services
- to establish an alternative means of communication in a large rural county[38]

The involvement of young people and foster carers throughout the development of this project has provided a valuable perspective to the local authority's thinking in terms of presentation of information to the general public, the sorts of resources that carers require and their training needs.

Children and young people have also been involved in the design of CareZone[39]. CareZone is The Who Cares? Trust's new secure online services for children in public care. It is an innovative package of child-centred services that aims to provide children with their own personal space. Visit www.thewhocarestrust.org.uk/carezone.htm

CareZone is the first service of its kind because it:

- features child-focused technology, developed with continuous input from children resulting in services they need and want
- provides children with their own personal space. Children in care are moved around frequently and personal possessions are often lost. CareZone provides a secure virtual space where these children can digitally store items of personal value
- builds trusted relationships with children over time, making it easier to ask for help if, and when, it's needed
- provides services that reduce the sense of isolation, as well as offering resources from a range of quality suppliers of information on health, care, well-being and education
- creates a community of care, including children, their carers and other allied professionals. All of these features are highly

secure and are accessed using Smart Card technology[39]

5.5.3. Practice and service delivery issues

Despite the development of ever more sophisticated means of communication, there is still a concern that young people's involvement in service planning is confined to the triangle of core support: young person, foster carer and social worker. It is within this triangle that children and young people exercise their influence on day-to-day decision making, having little or no opportunities to comment on service delivery more generally[10,40].

> **"If I was in charge of social services, I'd listen to them [people in care] first, see what they've got to say. I can't just make the rules on what I think is best for them."**
> **(young person in care[41])**

While managers express a commitment to young people having a greater say on service development, questions about the responsibility of managers and policy makers to create the right conditions for listening, learning and producing change remain unanswered, and the perspectives and experiences of young people are lost. The lack of systematic policies and practices to support and integrate the feedback from children and young people limits opportunities for young people to develop self-efficacy and a sense of involvement. Where evaluations do exist, the evidence suggests that the participation of children and young people is having little impact on decisions made in relation to agency policy and practice[10].

> **"... if I'm really honest ... I don't know what young people in our fostering services think or feel about the care they're getting."**
> **(senior social services manager[40])**

SCIE Position paper 3: *Has service user participation made a difference to social care services?*[10] brings together the key themes and findings from six literature reviews which looked at the impact of service user participation on change and improvement in social care services. Reviews on older people, people with learning difficulties, disabled people as well as children and young people, were also conducted as part of the project.

Messages from the research show the need for a range of models of involvement, depending on the level of activity to which participants wish to commit. What is important is that the choice is there, and that the involvement, or partnership, is real. Service user participation should relate clearly to a decision that the organisation plans to make and which the organisation is willing to make based on the views of the people they are consulting. It should be made clear what service users may or may not be able to change[10].

One of the aims of the Blueprint Project mentioned earlier is to move the attention of managers, policy makers and other professionals away from performance targets, back to what children want from the care system[41-3].

The Blueprint Project explored knowledge from three sources: what children and young people said, what policy makers and staff said, and research findings. These three elements were combined to produce a set of materials designed to help national and local agencies to provide child-centred care for looked-after children. All of the following Blueprint Project materials can be downloaded for free at www.vcc-uk.org:

- 'Start with the child, stay with the child: a blueprint for a child-centred approach to children and young people in public care'[41]
- 'Young people as partners in the Blueprint project: what young people had to say'[44]
- 'The care experience: summary of Blueprint's work on local authorities'[45]
- 'Try a different way'[46]: a set of 10 A4 sheets intended to be used by service providers as

ideas for discussion and possible implementation within their agencies

As part of the project, the canvassing of children's views has involved a participation programme overseen by a young person's participation and development worker and also a care leaver, Karen McBye. More than 20 looked-after young people have been trained as 'Blueprint reporters' who interview other looked-after young people about their views. From their interviews, some common themes have emerged:

- young people do not feel involved in review meetings
- young people experience problems with identity
- young people are not listened to or do not have their views taken into account[41]

> **"Young people get tired of never being listened to and the fact that, even when they are listened to, nothing ever changes. But I hope that something will come out of this one." (Jahnine Davis, Blueprint reporter[42])**

The research strand of the Blueprint Project has identified four key themes:

- relationships
- identity and individuality
- choice, control and competence
- dependence and independence

The project is moving away from the idea of finding the 'ideal family' and is instead looking at the importance of promoting "a strong, positive relationship with one person"[42]. The Blueprint team call this person a BFG or big friendly giant. BFGs should be chosen by the child and could ideally come from their existing social support network[43]. Family Group Conferences may represent an important method to identify BFGs. The Blueprint team suggest that where there is no obvious candidate, the child or young person would be helped to find someone to be their BFG – either someone who has worked with them in a

professional capacity or someone who is specifically appointed to be their BFG[43].

For children who have been placed with foster families with different religious, ethnic or cultural identities to their own, a BFG from the same background who can act as a 'cultural guide' may be particularly important. Gilligan highlights the story of Sue Jardine who, at 18 months, was adopted in the UK from Hong Kong. Upon reflecting on her own, often difficult, cultural experiences of growing up in a transracial placement, Sue suggests that a cultural guide such as a BFG would be a great help to a child growing up outside their culture[47].

Practice example
Cultural guides could help transracially placed children to know about … cultural festivals, show them how to cook, or how to approach concerns such as hair or skin care[47].

The importance of one interested adult

There are two important ways that a child-focused fostering service can offer secure and caring relationships to children and young people:

- by focusing on strategies that promote recruitment and retention of carers
- by providing a sustainable link between foster care and birth families

6.1. Foster carers

Secure attachments underpin the physical and emotional ties that support and sustain us as we grow and develop and can console us in times of distress[48,49]. Throughout our lives, we retain the need for support, encouragement and consolation. For children in the care system, it is not always immediately obvious that they have a secure base in the world[12]. Living in care may mean fragile relationships are broken, some never to recover[34].

6.1.1. Recruiting and retaining foster carers

Recruitment and retention strategies are the key means of finding and keeping the right kinds of foster carers, that is, foster carers who genuinely care for the children in their care and who, in some cases, are able to persist with and manage 'disturbed attachment behaviour' without the child or young person feeling rejected[8].

There are over 76,000 children and young people in public care on any given day in the UK, around 50,000 (64%) of whom live with 38,000 foster families[8]. The Fostering Network, a charity that represents foster carers, estimates that a further 8,000 foster carers are needed across the UK[50]. As part of the Choice Protects review, the DfES funded the Fostering Network to publish a guide to the recruitment and retention of foster carers[51], which examines the successful, and not so successful, recruitment and retention strategies used by local authorities across England.

Many black and minority ethnic children and children of mixed heritages are over-represented in the care system and have to wait too long for permanent placements. The British Association for Adoption and Fostering (BAAF) has launched an initiative aimed at recruiting black and minority ethnic foster carers. BAAF has been funded by the Association of London Government to actively support family placement professionals within local authorities and voluntary agencies in London to improve levels of recruitment of black and minority ethnic foster carers. Visit www.baaf.org.uk for more information[52].

Successful recruitment practice based on word-of-mouth, small cash incentives and targeted schemes (such as the initiative identified above) appear to work best for the recruitment of foster carers. The involvement of foster carers in recruitment campaigns has also been shown to have a positive impact on recruitment[7].

Research suggests that loss of foster carers is quite low, at 10% or less a year, which reflects the high level of commitment which carers have to foster children and the fulfilment that they get from caring. Support is crucial to the retention of foster carers, both on an everyday basis and in times of crisis, such as in the event of an allegation of abuse by a young person. Research studies highlight the importance of the following factors to foster carer retention:

- frequent contact with social workers
- feeling treated as colleagues
- guaranteed respite care
- the availability of out-of-hours telephone helplines
- well managed payment systems
- higher than average levels of pay
- easy access to specialist help and advice
- opportunities for taking part in training with other foster carers as a means to developing informal social support networks[7,8]

"If prospective foster carers could meet ... with more than a just a couple of people ... they could see that we actually support each other.... I think that if new people coming in realise that they don't have to do it by themselves, because foster carers talk to each other, [then] that is helpful." (foster carer in consultation group[54])

6.2. Birth families

The significance of birth families to foster children cannot be underestimated. Most fostering is short term with the primary aim of the child or young person returning home.

Good outcomes are dependent on the services provided to birth families as well the fostering services provided to children or young people.

6.2.1. Contact with birth families

Where fostering is longer term, foster children often feel ambivalent about how much, and in what ways, they want contact with their families. There are also wide differences between children about how much contact that they want: some want to move away from their families, some want to return to their birth families but still see a lot of their foster carers, others want to see something of their birth families but remain in foster care, and others just want to live at home.

There is a presumption in the 1989 Children Act that, wherever practicable, contact with birth families is required. Recent research evidence, however, suggests that contact requires very careful management and supervision to prevent any potential disruption to the young people's placement[8]. Some things that can help the management of contact include:

- paying attention to children's views of the importance of different family members, and ensuring the child's welfare and safety during contact
- setting clear boundaries for contact, distinguishing between contact with different family members, for different purposes and different contexts
- valuing the views of foster carers who are vital in helping children make sense of their family structures
- identifying and involving, where appropriate, other members of the young person's social support network who could provide care and attention[8]

In order to ensure a secure base for children, two important means of providing a determined link between foster children and the birth family are:

- making more use of, as well as supporting, family and friends' carers
- developing both supportive and therapeutic foster care schemes

6.2.2. Kinship care

Foster care with family or friends, otherwise known as kinship care, has the potential to build on existing relationships, make visits with birth families easier, protect black and minority ethnic children from losing touch with their ethnic and cultural identities, and spare the child or young person the trauma of being moved from their community and placed with strangers. Many young people describe a sense of security when living with their extended family which comes from the love, belonging and sense of identity they receive[55,56].

> **"I love to know that I belong to somebody, I'm loved by people and it's good to know that I have got somewhere to come after school that I call home." (young person being looked after by family carers[57])**

Kinship carers face unique barriers, however. They tend to be poorer (between two fifths and one third living in poverty), older (the majority are grandparents and over 50 years old), and they receive less in the way of services such as assessment, training and financial support than local authority carers. They may also face particular difficulties over contact with birth parents, difficulties that should be addressed within the care planning process[58,59].

In addition, extended family members continue to be overlooked in care planning meetings, suggesting that family members are not approached to act as carers. Yet research with care leavers shows that links with family networks remain important, particularly links with mothers, grandparents, siblings and aunts. One study of care leavers found that the majority could name a relative that they felt that they could rely on, which the family member was able to confirm. This study also found that in the majority of cases the young person's social worker had no idea why this so-called 'key kin' had not been invited to reviews[60].

Unfortunately, this failure to involve key kin ignores the role that families and friends have always been willing to play in looking after children who cannot live with or be cared for by their parents[59]. In particular, black commentators have expressed concern that the kinship arrangements of black and minority ethnic groups are overlooked by white social workers who may lack the knowledge or 'cultural competence' to understand the family formations or cultural expectations of black families[61].

> **"Black people have a tradition of kinship care, which, with the right economic resources to support it, could easily be transferred here, and indeed, transfers here even when resources are lacking." (Beverley Pravett-Goldstein, black rights activist and trainer[62])**

In light of the difficulties of recruiting foster carers, the use of family and friends may help resolve part of the shortfall in foster placements. Given the disproportionate number of black children in the care system, finding kinship placements that protect the ethnic identities of black and minority ethnic children may be particularly valuable[63].

Indeed, one qualitative study of 30 African-American kinship carers showed that support for the children in their care from the wider kin network helped promote positive child outcomes. This study also found that resilient children were more likely to live in families which were structured and which had clear boundaries and well-defined roles[64].

6.2.3. Keeping connections

As well as listening to the views of children and young people, another way workers can help children identify and connect with family members is the use of life story work with photographs of people in their social support network and moments from the young person's life gathered from network members. It is important that this work is ongoing and foster carers take photos of significant events such as birthdays, new schools and friends to help children and young people keep a record of their lives.

Life story work is about helping children express their feelings, preserving a sense of self and keeping connected with key kin, including foster carers. It can help children and young people make sense of their past and help them move forward[65]. It should be remembered, however, that life story work is a difficult and delicate area and is not appropriate for all children at particular stages of their lives.

The use of a social network map or use of an eco-map where the attachment network is mapped out and discussed is also a key means of helping foster children remain connected with family and friends[66]. This can be used independently or as part of life story work. Trigger questions could be developed that would be explored with the young person:

- Who is important to you in your life now?
- How close is each person to you?
- Who do you see?
- Who would you like to see?
- What changes would you like in the ways things are now?[29]

6.2.4. Family Group Conferences

Where there is conflict between what the child or young person wants by way of contact and what adults see as positive and helpful, then family group meetings may play a useful role in mediating the difficulties. In some local authorities, family group meetings have been formalised and take a much wider role in terms of decision making about the care and protection of the child or young person. These meetings are called Family Group Conferences (FGCs).

The Family Rights Group, which provides advice and support for families whose children are involved with social services, promotes the use of FGCs as a means to harness and build on the knowledge, strengths and resources in families and communities. Barnardo's, the Family Rights Group and NCH have produced extensive practice guidance on developing FGCs. For more information visit www.barnardos.org.uk, www.frg.org.uk and www.nch.org.uk[67]

FGCs can also help to 'discover' previously unknown family members who may be appropriate kinship carers. This method of recruitment is constrained, however, because of the limited use of FGCs. At the moment, within the UK there are just 59 FGC projects registered with the Family Rights Group, across a variety of statutory and volunteers organisations.

> **Practice example**
> FGCs can help to identify kinship carers. These conferences have been instrumental in discovering family and friends willing to be involved in the care of looked-after children[68].

6.2.5. Practice and service delivery issues

Kinship care is not a cure-all. Evidence from Knowledge review 5: *Fostering success: An exploration of the research literature in foster care*[8] suggests that research on outcomes is equivocal. Some studies report that children placed with kinship carers experience fewer psychological problems, while other studies suggest that children are more likely to experience further abuse or neglect. Early research suggested that breakdowns were uncommon but recent work suggests that placements are as likely to break down as those provided by strangers. Careful consideration should be paid to the relative strengths and weaknesses of kinship and non-kinship care, focusing on ways to support the placement so that the young person can achieve 'emotional permanence' or a sense of security from being loved[8].

6.3. Foster carers and birth families

Another way of providing a more determined link between foster care and family is the development of specialist schemes that provide support to the birth family as well as to the fostered child or young person. Specialist schemes include:

- support foster care where the foster carers are seen as a support to the entire family
- treatment foster care which includes the ability to train birth parents in the same approach

6.3.1. Support foster care

Foster carers can work with birth parents in a variety of ways. Some of the most valued forms of cooperation are the provision of short breaks or respite care, most commonly, but not exclusively, for the parents of disabled children. More recently, the development of 'support care schemes', specifically Bradford Support Care and Birmingham's Neighbourhood Care Service, have been working with teenage service users and their families to provide flexible breaks and prevent long-term family breakdown[7].

Support foster care schemes aim to provide:

- support to families in crisis
- placements that are time limited and agreed

- a wide variety of placement options from occasional day care to regular weekends
- a tailor-made service for each family[7]

Practice example
Bradford Support Care provides a part-time, flexible fostering service. This service aims to prevent long-term family breakdown by offering families support from part-time foster carers for planned, time-limited periods[70].

Traditional foster placements risk removing young people from their families full time for lengthy periods. Generally, such placements were not flexible enough to meet the needs of families, especially lone mothers who were struggling to cope with their adolescent offspring in a situation where there were long-standing difficulties related to family conflict, school problems, behavioural difficulties, mental health problems and drug and alcohol issues. Support foster care aims to alleviate some of these difficulties. The DfES has funded an evaluation of support foster care[71].

6.3.2. Treatment foster care

Some fostering schemes have been developed to provide specialised or therapeutic foster care. These schemes are marked by a number of features:

- an above-average level of support, training and remuneration of carers
- an often teenage user group with challenging behaviour
- a coordinated method of working that aims to treat behaviours in home, school and community
- clinical staff, including psychiatrists that support the placement
- a specified length of stay[8]

Treatment foster care is distinct from traditional foster care. Fostering has always been about providing nurturing, safe, and in some cases, custodial care for children who require placement outside of their family. Its primary aim has been the care and protection of children. Children are referred to treatment foster care programmes, on the other hand, in order to specifically address their serious levels of emotional, behavioural and medical problems.

It aims to reduce such problems through a coordinated programme of working, maintain young people in their placement and to support birth families to care for the young person. The DfES is currently funding an £11 million pilot programme of treatment foster care. For more information visit www.dfes.gov.uk

Practice example

Treatment foster care aims to provide a locally based intervention for looked-after young people using innovative practice to reduce serious behavioural problems. The DfES programme will use a similar model to that developed in the US and will be targeted at young people who are:

- 11-16 years old
- displaying severe levels of challenging or anti-social behaviour, and/or
- self-harming, and/or
- involved in crime and who may be at risk of receiving a custodial sentence.

Treatment foster care is an intervention targeted at young people for whom more conventional approaches do not offer an effective solution. Such young people might in the past have been considered not fit for fostering. Existing treatment foster care programmes, such as that pioneered by the Maudsley Hospital in London, suggest positive outcomes in terms of placement stability and education in particular[72].

There is a long tradition of local authority and voluntary organisation collaboration with respect to services for children and young people with complex needs. Voluntary organisations often pioneer innovative developments which local authorities commission for their most troubled and troublesome teenagers[4]. Specialist schemes which offer the intensive support of carers, training of carers, social workers and where appropriate birth-parents in the same social learning approach combined with close attention to schooling have been positively evaluated in comparison to residential care in relation to both young offenders and disturbed children[8].

7

Feeling happy at school

After their family, the most important institution in the lives of most children and young people is their school[73]. Teachers and other adults in schools can listen to students, refrain from judgement and develop strong, caring relationships with them. The offer of a close relationship with a school counsellor appears to be a key resilience-enhancing factor for foster children.

> **Key reading**
> *Education matters – for everyone working with children in public care*[74]
> This book provides social workers with essential information about education and provides education professionals with information about social care.
>
> *Believe in me*[75]
> *Believe in me* is aimed at designated teachers and other professionals concerned with the literacy development of young people in care.

7.1. Success at school

Success at school is crucial to the future opportunities of foster children. Yet the current educational achievements of foster children are low, with nearly half of all children in care leaving school with no qualifications at all[76]. It should be remembered that the scholastic difficulties of foster children often precede placement in foster care but are not apparently improved by it. In some cases, placement in foster care may exacerbate scholastic difficulties especially when children are moved to new schools closer to the homes of foster carers which can disrupt the continuity of their education[8].

It should also be remembered that the educational attainment of foster children is now improving, supported by the introduction of educational targets by the DfES and in Wales, the National Assembly[77]. The research literature suggests that there is some agreement on the factors that are likely to produce improved educational outcomes for looked-after children. These include:

- encouragement from carers and the presence of other children who can model academic involvement and success
- the presence of 'educational supports' (someone attending school events, access to local library, information on education rights and entitlements)
- contact with an educational psychologist reduces the likelihood of foster placement breakdown[8]

> **"My foster carer helped me a lot ... she made me more confident in my school work." (11-year-old girl[3])**

Users of fostering services confirm that these factors can make an impact. Voices from Care Cymru, a user group of young people who are, or who have been looked after, in Wales, organised two conferences to consult with children and young people about the National Assembly for Wales' Children First programme.

A total of 97 children and young people were involved and their experience of education was a key theme, highlighting that young people wanted to succeed in school. You can find out more from the conferences by visiting www.vfcc.org.uk

The kinds of things that help young people to achieve include:

- encouragement to do well, including the expectation that young people in care will achieve 5 GCSEs
- getting help at home and at school, such as help from foster carers or access to an educational psychologist or a counsellor
- support to stay at college, financial as well as emotional[5]

The Fostering Network is working with local authorities in Scotland to develop schemes that find mentors for young people leaving the care system. Mentors can offer advice, guidance and support to young people, helping them to build on their existing talents and abilities and develop new ones, including attending college[78].

Practice example
A mentoring relationship can be an important turning point in lives of young people … for example, a teenage girl living in a sink estate had a father frequently in prison and a mother who was chemically dependent. She was doing poorly at school and a likely candidate for early drop out. Out of the blue she made a positive connection with a new young English teacher. With her encouragement and support, the girl caught up and is talking seriously (and realistically) about doing law in university. (case study provided by practitioner[79])

7.2. The good and bad news about school

The Social Exclusion Unit and The Who Cares? Trust carried out a consultation exercise into the educational experiences of children in care. Around 2,000 responses were received, making this one of the largest direct consultations undertaken with this group of children. See the results at www.socialexclusionunit.gov.uk

The consultation found that children were positive about their education, attended school regularly, and were given support by adults. However, there are problems around the number of children who are changing schools, bullying and exclusions[80].

Key themes include the following: The good news

Children in care consider education to be important, largely for career reasons:
- 97% said that they thought education was important
- 61% of these cited career prospects as the main reason.

Many of the children lived in an environment that already had some of the factors we associate with supporting a successful education:
- 91% had a quiet place to do their homework
- 81% had help with their schoolwork
- 71% had a computer where they lived.

Most children in care said they had adults that they could confide in or ask advice from:
- 87% said that there was a member of staff who they could talk to at school.

The bad news
A high proportion of children had been excluded from school (this includes self-perceived, unofficial and fixed term exclusions as well as permanent exclusions):
- 37% had at some point been excluded from school
- 51% of these said that more support would have helped them not get excluded.

19

The majority of children in care had been the victims of bullying. Most had told someone and this stopped the bullying, but for a significant minority it did not:

- 62% had been bullied
- 80% of those who had been bullied told someone
- 67% of those who told someone said this stopped the bullying[80]

7.3. Practice and service delivery issues

Published alongside the Green Paper *Every child matters*, the Social Exclusion Unit's (SEU) report on *Better education for children in care* aims to improve stability in care and support at school in order to help boost education and prospects for children in care, one of the most deprived groups of young people.

The measures outlined in the SEU report mean that children in care will get better personal education plans to support learning needs and more books to help learning at home. Designated teachers will encourage children in care to stay on at school after the age of 16 and more work placements will be available to help children in care fulfil their potential. The reports include the following:

- 'A better education for children in care'[76]
- 'A better education for children in care – summary'[81]
- 'Smart future' (young people's version)[3]

In order to support local authorities as they take action to improve the education of children in care, the SEU has also produced a practice guide called 'A better education for children in care: the issues'[82] which outlines the key issues emerging from their report and the steps some local authorities are taking to address them.

In the past there has been a perception that Independent Fostering Agencies (IFAs) have led the way in terms of providing additional educational support to foster children. In a survey of 55 IFAs, just over half of these agencies had employed an educational liaison

officer and one fifth had an on-site school[83]. More recently, many local authorities have made big advances in these areas. The SEU has published seven fact sheets that outline examples of existing good practice from local authorities.

The fact sheets cover the following areas:

- 'Access to out of school activities'[84]
- 'Access to school'[85]
- 'Early years'[86]
- 'Health'[87]
- 'Post 16'[88]
- 'Support in education'[89]
- 'Support at home'[90]

Practice examples
Hampshire County Council has appointed a lead officer responsible for the education of children in public care, a dedicated staff group of teachers and a community therapist for looked-after children.

Cheshire County Council has an Education Support and Development Team that aims to improve educational achievement and opportunity. It includes an educational psychologist and three teachers who provide direct support and advice to children and foster carers[91]

8

Conclusion

This resource guide looked at how professionals can make a difference to young people's experience of foster care. It has looked at:

- how you (a childcare professional) matter
- why you matter
- ways in which you can make a difference

Research shows that focusing on the strengths of young people is crucial to future outcomes. This means focusing on 'resilience factors', or things that help children and young people do well in unpromising conditions.

Professionals play a crucial role in promoting the strengths of young people by supporting caring relationships, ensuring that school is a positive experience and findings ways of bolstering self-esteem and self-efficacy.

The resource guide has aimed to benefit your practice by:

- helping you to engage in debates in your own agencies about what policies will best serve children and their families
- providing a short, accessible review of the knowledge base on adopting a resilience-based approach to assist you in your own cases
- identifying practice examples of where social work and social care agencies work positively to support the strengths of children and their families

The guide has looked at ways that you, as a childcare professional, can help foster the future success of fostered children and young people.

References

1 Wilson, K., Sinclair, I., Taylor, C., Pithouse, A. and Sellick, C. (2004) *Fostering success: An exploration of the research literature in foster care*, Knowledge review 5, London: Social Care Institute for Excellence, p 60.

2 The Who Cares? Trust (1993) *Not just a name: The views of young people in foster and residential care*, London: National Consumer Council, p 78.

3 SEU (Social Exclusion Unit) (2003) 'Smart future' (available at www.socialexclusionunit.gov.uk/ publications/reports/pdfs/SmartFuture.pdf, accessed 11 February 2004), p 8.

4 Sellick, C. and Howell, D. (2003) *Innovative, tried and tested: A review of good practice in fostering*, Knowledge review 4, London: Social Care Institute for Excellence, p 35.

5 Voice from Care Cymru (2001) 'Children what? Looked after young people's responses to the National assembly for Wales Children First Programme' (available at www.voicesfromcarecymru.org.uk/ childrenswhat.htm, accessed 25 June 2004).

6 Wilson, K., Sinclair, I., Taylor, C., Pithouse, A. and Sellick, C. (2004) *Fostering success: An exploration of the research literature in foster care*, Knowledge review 5, London: Social Care Institute for Excellence, p 1.

7 Sellick, C. and Howell, D. (2003) *Innovative, tried and tested: A review of good practice in fostering*, Knowledge review 4, London: Social Care Institute for Excellence.

8 Wilson, K., Sinclair, I., Taylor, C., Pithouse, A. and Sellick, C. (2004) *Fostering success: An exploration of the research literature in foster care*, Knowledge review 5, London: Social Care Institute for Excellence.

9 Rushton, A. (2003) *The adoption of looked after children: A scoping review of research*, Knowledge review 2, London: Social Care Institute for Excellence.

10 Carr, S. (2004) *Has service user participation made a difference to social care services?*, Position paper 3, London: Social Care Institute for Excellence.

11 Gilligan, R. (ed) (2000) 'Promoting resilience in children in foster care', in G. Kelly and R. Gilligan (eds) *Issues in foster care: Policy, practice and research*, London: Jessica Kingsley Publishers.

12 Gilligan, R. (1998) 'Beyond permanence? The importance of resilience in child placement and planning', in M. Hill and M. Shaw (eds) *Signposts in adoption: Policy, practice and research issues*, London: BAAF.

13 DfES (Department for Education and Skills) (2002) 'Choice Protects' (available at www.dfes.gov.uk/choiceprotects/, accessed 11 February 2004).

14 National Assembly for Wales (1999) 'Children First' (available at www.childrenfirst.wales.gov.uk/content/ about.htm, accessed 25 June 2004).

15 Department of Health, Department of Education and Skills, and Home Office (2000) *Framework for the assessment of children in need and their families*, London: The Stationery Office.

16 Franklin, B. (2002) 'Children's rights and media wrongs: changing representations of children and the developing rights agenda', in B. Franklin (ed) *The new handbook of children's rights: Comparative policy and practice*, London: Routledge.

17 James, A. and Prout, A. (1997) *Constructing and reconstructing childhood: Contemporary issues in the sociological study of childhood* (2nd edn), London: Falmer Press.

18 James, A., Jenks, C. and Prout, A. (1997) *Theorizing childhood*, London: Polity Press.

19 Henry, D.L. (2001) 'Resilient children: what they tell us about coping with maltreatment', *Social Work in Health Care*, vol 34, no 3/4, pp 283-98.

20 Miller, D. (2002) 'Journeys from childhood to midlife: risk, resilience and recovery', *British Journal of Social Work*, vol 32, no 5, pp 647-8.

21 Reed-Taylor, E. and Stronge, J.H. (2002) 'Homeless students and resilience: staff perspectives on individual and environmental factors', *Journal of Children and Poverty*, vol 8, no 2, pp 159-74.

22 De Civita, M. (2000) 'Promoting resilience: a vision of care', *Reclaiming Children and Youth: Journal of Emotional and Behavioral Problems*, vol 9, no 2, pp 76-8, 83.

23 O'Neill, C. (2001) 'Promoting resilience: a resource guide on working with children in the care system', *Australian Social Work*, vol 54, no 3, pp 124-5.

24 Lambert, C. (2001) *Promoting resilience in 'looked-after children'*, Norwich: University of East Anglia.

25 Thompson, N. (2002) 'Promoting resilience: a resource guide on working with children in the care system', *Child and Family Social Work*, vol 7, no 1, pp 65-6.

26 Newman, T. (2002) *Promoting resilience: A review of effective strategies for child care services*, Exeter: Centre for Evidence-Based Social Services, University of Exeter.

27 Newman, T. and Blackburn, B. (2002) 'Transitions in the lives of children and young people: resilience factors', *Interchange*, vol 78: Scottish Executive Education Department.

28 Gilligan, R. (2001) *Promoting resilience: A resource guide on working with children in the care system*, London: BAAF.

29 Daniel, B., Sally, W. and Robbie, G. (1999) '"It's just common sense isn't it?" Exploring ways of putting resilience into action', *Adoption and Fostering*, vol 23, no 3, pp 6-15.

30 Ungar, M. (2001) 'The social construction of resilience among problem youth in out-of-home placement: a study of health-enhancing deviance', *Child and Youth Care Forum*, vol 30, no 3, pp 137-54.

31 Butler, J. (2004) 'Remembering birthdays helps self esteem', recipient L. Bostock (personal communication).

32 A National Voice (2003) *Amplify*, Manchester: A National Voice.

33 Gilligan, R. (2000) 'The importance of listening to the child in foster care', in G. Kelly and R. Gilligan (eds) *Issues in foster care*, London: Jessica Kingsley, pp 50-8.

34 Cairns, K. (2002) *Attachment, trauma and resilience: Therapeutic caring for children*, London: BAAF.

35 Dowling, E. (1993) 'Are family therapist listening to the young? A psychological perspective', *Journal of Family Therapy*, vol 15, pp 403-11.

36 Parker, R., Ward, H., Jackson, S., Aldgate, J. and Wedge, P. (1991) *Looking after children, assessing outcomes in child care: The report of an independent working party established by the Department of Health*, London: Department of Health/HMSO.

37 The Fostering Network and The Who Cares? Trust (2002) *Listen then commission*, London: Department of Health.

38 Sellick, C. and Howell, D. (2003) *Innovative, tried and tested: A review of good practice in fostering*, Knowledge review 4, London: Social Care Institute for Excellence, pp 35-7.

39 The Who Cares? Trust (2002) *CareZone*, London: The Who Cares? Trust.

40 Padbury, P. and Frost, N. (2002) *Solving problems in foster care: Key issues for young people, foster carers and social services*, London: The Children's Society, p 73.

41 Voice for the Child in Care (2004) 'Start with the child, stay with the child: a blueprint for a child-centred approach to children and young people in public care' (available at www.vcc-uk.org/docimages/44.pdf, accessed 6 July 2004), p 8.

42 Winchester, R. (2003) 'Let's hear it from the experts', *Community Care*, 26 June-2 July, pp 26-8.

43 Voice for the Child in Care (2003) *Blueprint project: A blueprint for child centred care*, London: VCC with NCB.

44 Voice for the Child in Care (2004) 'Young people as partners in the Blueprint project: what young people had to say' (available at www.vcc-uk.org/docimages/45.pdf, accessed 6 July 2004).

45 Voice for the Child in Care (2004) 'The care experience: summary of Blueprint's work on local authorities' (available at www.vcc-uk.org/docimages/33.pdf, accessed 6 July 2004).

46 Voice for the Child in Care (2004) 'Try a different way' (available at www.vcc-uk.org/docimages/34.pdf, accessed 6 July 2004).

47 Jardine, S. (1999) 'Transracial placements: an adoptee's perspective', in R. Barn (ed) *Working with black children and adolescents need*, London: BAAF, p 155.

48 Rutter, M. (1985) 'Resilience in the face of adversity: protective factors and resistance to psychiatric disorder', *Community Mental Health*, vol 2, pp 163-82.

49 Rutter, M. (1999) 'Resilience concepts and findings implications for family therapy', *Journal of Family Therapy*, vol 21, no 2, pp 119-44.

50 The Fostering Network (2003) 'Shortage of foster carers' (available at www.thefostering.net/comdir/cditem.cfm?NID=453, accessed 11 March 2004).

51 The Fostering Network and Department for Education and Skills (2004) *Good practice guidelines on the recruitment of foster carers*, London: Department for Education and Skills.

52 BAAF (British Association for Adoption and Fostering) (2004) 'Association of London Government black and minority ethnic carer recruitment project' (available at www.baaf.org.uk/, accessed 11 March 2004).

53 Sellick, C. and Howell, D. (2003) *Innovative, tried and tested: A review of good practice in fostering*, Knowledge review 4, London: Social Care Institute for Excellence, p 11.

54 Wilson, K., Sinclair, I., Taylor, C., Pithouse, A. and Sellick, C. (2004) *Fostering success: An exploration of the research literature in foster care*, Knowledge review 5, London: Social Care Institute for Excellence, p 62.

55 Broad, B. (ed) (2001) *Kinship care: The placement choice for children and young people*, Lyme Regis: Russell House.

56 Broad, B., Hayes, R. and Rushforth, C. (2001) *Kith and kin: Kinship care for vulnerable young people*, York: Joseph Rowntree Foundation/National Children's Bureau.

57 Philpot, T. and Broad, B. (2003) *Family problems, family solutions: Kinship care for children in need: An agenda for change*, Leicester: De Montfort University, p 6.

58 Richards, A. (2001) *Second time around: A survey of grandparents raising their grandchildren*, London: Family Rights Group.

59 Richards, A. and Tapsfield, R. (2003) *Funding family and friends care: The way forward*, London: Family Rights Group.

60 Philpot, T. and Broad, B. (2003) *Family problems, family solutions: Kinship care for children in need: An agenda for change*, Leicester: De Montfort University, p 8.

61 Philpot, T. and Broad, B. (2003) *Family problems, family solutions: Kinship care for children in need: An agenda for change*, Leicester: De Montfort University.

62 Philpot, T. and Broad, B. (2003) *Family problems, family solutions: Kinship care for children in need: An agenda for change*, Leicester: De Montfort University, p 5.

63 Richards, A. and Ince, L. (2000) *Overcoming the obstacles: Looked after children: Quality services for black and ethnic minority children and their families*, London: Family Rights Group.

64 Johnson-Garner, M.Y. and Meyers, S.A. (2003) 'What factors contribute to the resilience of African-American children within kinship care?', *Child and Youth Care Forum*, vol 32, no 6, pp 255-69.

65 Arvin Publications (undated) *My life book*, Arlington: Arvin Publications.

66 Hartman, A. (1995) 'Diagrammatic assessment of family relationship', *Families in Society: the Journal of Contemporary Human Services*, vol 76, no 3, pp 111-22.

67 Barnardo's, Family Rights Group, and NCH (National Childrens Home) (2002) *Family group conferences: Principles and practice guidance*, London: Barnardo's.

68 Philpot, T. and Broad, B. (2003) *Family problems, family solutions: Kinship care for children in need: An agenda for change*, Leicester: De Montfort University, p 9.

69 Wilson, K., Sinclair, I., Taylor, C., Pithouse, A. and Sellick, C. (2004) *Fostering success: An exploration of the research literature in foster care*, Knowledge review 5, London: Social Care Institute for Excellence, pp 38-9.

70 Sellick, C. and Howell, D. (2003) *Innovative, tried and tested: A review of good practice in fostering*, Knowledge review 4, London: Social Care Institute for Excellence, p 22.

71 Fry, E. (2003) *Support foster care: A research proposal*, London: Fostering Network.

72 Surrey Children's Service (2003) 'Treatment foster care in Surrey' (available at www.surrey-camhs.org.uk/docs/fos_care.html, accessed 9 March 2004).

73 Minnard, C.V. (2002) 'A strong building: foundation of protective factors in schools', *Children and Schools*, vol 24, no 4, pp 233-46.

74 The Who Cares? Trust (undated) *Education matters - for everyone working with children in public care*, London: The Who Cares? Trust.

75 The Who Cares? Trust (undated) *Believe in me*, London: The Who Cares? Trust.

76 SEU (Social Exclusion Unit) (2003) 'A better education for children in care' (available at www.socialexclusionunit.gov.uk/publications/reports/html/CinCmainfinal/contents.html, accessed 11 March 2004).

77 SEU (Social Exclusion Unit) (2003) 'Targets' (available at www.socialexclusionunit.gov.uk/ young_people/young_people/ Fact%20Sheet-Target.pdf, accessed 11 March 2004).

78 Grossman, J. and Tierney, J. (1998) 'Does mentoring work? An impact study of the brothers and sisters programme', *Evaluation Review*, vol 22, no 3, pp 403-26.

79 Gilligan, R. (2001) *Promoting resilience: A resource on working with children in the care system*, London: BAAF, p 32.

80 SEU (Social Exclusion Unit) and The Who Cares? Trust (2002) *Report on education of children and young people in care*, London: SEU.

81 SEU (Social Exclusion Unit) (2003) 'A better education for children in care – summary' (available at www.socialexclusionunit.gov.uk/ publications/reports/pdfs/ CinCSummaryFinal.pdf, accessed 11 March 2004).

82 SEU (Social Exclusion Unit) (2003) 'A better education for children in care: the issues' (available at www.socialexclusionunit.gov.uk/ young_people/young_people/ DissLeaflet.pdf, accessed 11 March 2004).

83 Sellick, C. and Connolly, J. (2002) 'Independent fostering agencies uncovered: the findings of a national study', *Child and Family Social Work*, vol 7, no 2, pp 107-20.

84 SEU (Social Exclusion Unit) (2003) 'Access to out of school activities' (available at www.socialexclusionunit.gov.uk/ young_people/young_people/ Fact%20Sheet-OutofSchool.pdf, accessed 11 March 2004).

85 SEU (Social Exclusion Unit) (2003) 'Access to school' (available at www.socialexclusionunit.gov.uk/ young_people/young_people/ Fact%20Sheet-Access_School.pdf, accessed 11 March 2004).

86 SEU (Social Exclusion Unit) (2003) 'Early years' (available at www.socialexclusionunit.gov.uk/ young_people/young_people/ Fact%20Sheet-Early%20Years.pdf, accessed 11 March 2004).

87 SEU (Social Exclusion Unit) (2003) 'Health' (available at www.socialexclusionunit.gov.uk/ young_people/young_people/ Fact%20Sheet-Health.pdf, accessed 11 March 2004).

88 SEU (Social Exclusion Unit) (2003) 'Post 16' (available at www.socialexclusionunit.gov.uk/ young_people/young_people/ Fact%20Sheet-Post16.pdf, accessed 11 March 2004).

89 SEU (Social Exclusion Unit) (2003) 'Support in education' (available at www.socialexclusionunit.gov.uk/ young_people/young_people/ Fact%20Sheet-Supp-Education.pdf, accessed 11 March 2004).

90 SEU (Social Exclusion Unit) (2003) 'Support at home' (available at www.socialexclusionunit.gov.uk/ young_people/young_people/ Fact%20Sheet-Support_Home.pdf, accessed 11 March 2004).

91 Sellick, C. and Howell, D. (2003) *Innovative, tried and tested: A review of good practice in fostering*, Knowledge review 4, London: Social Care Institute for Excellence, p 32.

92 Daniel, B. and Wassell, S. (2002) *Assessing and promoting resilience in vulnerable children: A 3 volume set: The early years, The school years, Adolescence*, London: Jessica Kingsley Publishers.

Appendix 1: Membership of the SCIE Advisory Group on Fostering

- **Professor Malcolm Hill**, Director, Glasgow Centre for the Child and Society, Glasgow University
- **Iris Amoah**, Team Manager, Fostering Team, Hackney Social Services
- **Mark Burgress**, service user representative, A National Voice
- **Beverley Clarke**, Health Visitor and Team Advisor, Lambeth Primary Care Trust
- **Clare Chamberlain**, Director, The Blueprint Project for a Child-Centred Public Care System
- **Vanessa Courtney**, Senior Manager, Portsmouth City Council, Association of Directors of Social Services
- **Rhonwyn Dobbing**, Professional Advisor, Social Services Inspectorate for Wales
- **Helen Hibbert**, Education Development Manager, The Who Cares? Trust
- **Hilary Rock**, Team Manager, Fostering Support Team, Waltham Forest Social Services Department
- **Emma de Zoete**, Policy Lead, Choice Protects Team, Department for Education and Skills
- **Sue Jardine**, service user representative, Association for Transracially Adopted and Fostered People (ATRAP)
- **Bill Kilgallon**, foster carer and Chief Executive, Social Care Institute for Excellence (SCIE)
- **Sue Gourvish**, Head of Development, The Fostering Network
- **Robert Tapsfield**, Chief Executive, Family Rights Group (now Chief Executive of The Fostering Network)
- **Benni-Jo Tyler**, service user representative, A National Voice
- **John Simmonds**, Head of Research, British Association for Adoption and Fostering (BAAF)
- **Marcia Spencer**, Independent Training Consultant, Talawa Social Work Training and Consultancy

Appendix 2:
Key reading

Gilligan, R. (2001) *Promoting resilience: A resource guide on working with children in the care system*[28].

This book is packed with practical ideas for how to improve the quality of life of children in care. It carries two key messages of hope:

- the lives of children can be made better
- what social workers and carers do – even the little things – can make a difference

Cairns, K. (2002) *Attachment, trauma and resilience: Therapeutic caring for children*[34].

This book is written from the perspective of a foster carer and describes affirming personal resilience with children who find solitude difficult, encouraging social inclusion and personal and social efficacy, and the development of tranquillity, joy and a sense of wonder.

Daniel, B. and Wassell, S. (2002) *Assessing and promoting resilience in vulnerable children: A 3 volume set: The early years, The school years, Adolescence*[92].

This clear and practical workbook shows the importance of encouraging resilience in children and young people who live in challenging circumstances.

Newman, T. (2002) *Promoting resilience: A review of effective strategies for child care services*[26].

This report reviews the strategies, inventions and approaches that can help promote the resilience of children and young people. It addresses the following questions:

- What is resilience and why it is important to child welfare services?
- Why do some children and young people resist and overcome stressful episodes while others suffer long-term damage?
- How can a child welfare service promote resilience?

Also available from SCIE

Resource Guide No 2
Involving service users and carers in social work education
Better outcomes for service users and carers are fundamental to the recent reforms in social work education. The Social Care Institute for Excellence (SCIE) is supporting the new degree in social work by providing a series of reviews and guides on the best way of educating and training social workers.

This Resource guide outlines ways of involving service users and carers in all aspects of the design and delivery of the social work degree programmes. It focuses on how partnerships between higher education institutions (HEIs) and service user and carer organisations can be developed and sustained. It covers the values, principles and practicalities of participation, outlining a range of approaches to creating active and purposeful partnerships.

Paperback 210x297mm • 48 pages • ISBN 1 904812 07 4 • March 2004

Resource Guide No 3
Teaching and learning communication skills in social work education
Good communication, both oral and written, is at the heart of best practice in social work. Communication skills are essential for establishing effective and respectful relationships with service users, for assessments, decision making and joint working with colleagues and other professionals. The social work degree puts a strong emphasis on communicating well with service users and carers and it is a core learning outcome.

SCIE is supporting the degree in social work by providing a series of resource guides on the best ways of educating and training social workers.

This resource guide is based on findings from a knowledge review that examined this critical area of social work education. It signposts new ways of working in teaching and learning communication skills on the new social work degree.

The guide is primarily for programme providers of the social work degree including service users and carers involved in the planning and delivery of the social work degree programmes. It may also be of interest to those offering practice placement opportunities, student social workers, and others involved in skills development.

Paperback 210x297mm • 84 pages • ISBN 1 904812 08 2 • June 2004

Full versions of all SCIE publications, including titles on social work education, are available on the SCIE website and in print from SCIE.

Further details are available from:
Social Care Institute for Excellence
1st Floor, Goldings House
2 Hay's Lane
London SE1 2HB

Tel: 020 7089 6840
Fax: 020 7089 6841
www.scie.org.uk

Other formats of this publication can be made available on request